the first year of life

including
SPECIAL EARLY LEARNING SUPPLEMENT
by Dr. Burton L. White

CASTLE
BOOKS

Published by
CASTLE BOOKS
A Division of
BOOK SALES, INC.
110 Enterprise Avenue
Secaucus, New Jersey 07094

ISBN 0-89009-476-4
COPYRIGHT © MCMLXXXI BY AMERICAN BABY BOOKS
ALL RIGHTS RESERVED
THIS EDITION IS PUBLISHED BY CASTLE BOOKS,
A DIVISION OF BOOK SALES, INC.
BY ARRANGEMENT WITH AMERICAN BABY BOOKS.
a b c d e f g h
CASTLE 1981 EDITION
MANUFACTURED IN THE UNITED STATES OF AMERICA

Copyright © 1981 American Baby Books

57371

contents

introduction

You are about to embark on one of life's most thrilling adventures—the launching of a totally new human being. If this is your first encounter with parenthood, you are undoubtedly faced with an array of vague doubts, anxieties, fears and more than a little ambivalence. Little wonder: there is probably less preparedness for parenthood today than for any other endeavor of one's lifetime.

To the family-oriented men and women of generations past, the raising of babies was automatically one of life's commitments, and every female somehow "just knew" how to be a mother. But trends toward a more mechanized, urbanized, relocated, liberated, career-oriented society have changed all that. Today's babies are far more likely to be carefully planned. At the same time, today's young adults are *less* likely to have become accustomed to the phenomenon of parenthood.

Moreover, even an available and willing "teacher" doesn't necessarily signal an equally willing learner. Modern-day parents and parents-to-be are increasingly aware that babies are not to be raised according to a "recipe." Formal education is of little help either—often it has only provided a greater knowledge of what might "go wrong." What is of greatest concern to today's parents is how they can best channel their child's very personal mode of development and help give him the foundation to become a well-adjusted, happy, productive member of society.

This publication is not a how-to in terms of feeding or diapering. Rather it is a how-to in terms of learning how to enjoy, how to understand, how to cope with and how to appreciate each new facet of your baby's development. In so doing, our sincere hope is that you will reap greater pleasure from the many satisfactions of parenthood. What we have attempted to do here is to acquaint you as new parents with what you can reasonably expect of your new baby, and at approximately what stage of his or her development. The more familiar you are with the fine points of the growth processes, the more easily you will be able to understand and communicate with your child—and the fewer will be the difficulties.

But remember—your baby won't have read the text! The most striking thing about a newborn is how different each is from every other. Yours won't do the same things at the same time or in the same way as anyone else's baby. Most assuredly, no baby will follow the precise pattern presented here.

The material has been arranged by months for the sake of convenience only. Throughout the first year of baby's life, some parents will be reviewing back chapters, others will be reading ahead, most will be doing both. Specific kinds of development differ with the individual. The baby who is "slow" to roll over, for example, may be unusually "advanced" in vocal ability or finger coordination.

While timetables vary considerably, *sequence* of development tends to remain fairly similar. But even here, some types of behavior may occur in different order or perhaps not at all. Crib-rocking, for instance, while common, does not occur in all babies. An adverse reaction to strangers is not as predictable as once thought: the same baby may exhibit different responses every few days.

Attempts by parents to "push" their baby's development in any way are likely to be not only fruitless but also confusing to the child. More important than *when* a new growth event occurs is *what* a baby does with it. For instance, the ability to grasp is, in itself, of lesser value than how the infant puts his newfound ability to use in exploring his environment.

A brand-new, inexperienced parent may well feel totally lacking in "natural" or "motherly" feelings. This is not an unusual reaction. Any new kind of relationship takes time to establish itself. There is no reason to worry if you feel uncomfortable or unsure about what such natural parental impulses are supposed to be. Simply offer your baby the same kind of consideration you would if he were *not* an infant. You presumably know how to live and comfort your husband, best friend or maiden aunt. Your baby, too, is a *person*, not some alien creature who has just arrived from outer space (the myth of the stork notwithstanding). The parent/child relationship will find its way in due time.

But do spend some extra "fun" time with your baby whenever possible! The kinds of circumstances of his early environment can easily result in a more interested, cheerful and alert child. The importance of personal stimulation cannot be overemphasized—it is far more valuable than expensive toys. Many studies in recent years repeatedly demonstrate that cuddling is vital to both the physical and psychological welfare of an infant, although scientists have yet to determine exactly why. More obvious are the effects of parent/child interaction in the gradual establishment of communication patterns. An outstretched hand, tightly flexed legs, a high-pitched gurgle, a frantic huffing and puffing—each conveys a message.

Leading child authorities today are in almost unanimous agreement that a baby cannot be spoiled during the first half-year of life. (This is a rather different attitude from the famed Dr. Spock's controversial—and rather lone—contention of a generation ago that an infant could not be spoiled during his first three months.) For a number of years now, studies have indicated that prompt response to an infant's crying affords him greater security. He more quickly learns that comfort is forthcoming, and as he matures, consequently cries *less* and becomes less demanding than does a baby who has not met with as much reassurance.

As you read through the following chapters, we stress again that you must continually consider the individuality of your own child. Don't expect to have a "book baby"—and by the same token don't expect to be a "book mother" (or father).

Not only is each infant unique but so is each relationship the infant has with those about him—his mother, his father, a sibling, a grandparent. The "latest authority" can never have all the answers for *your* baby—so don't be afraid to follow your own instincts and common sense. The most astonishing fact about infancy is how alike babies are by being different—and probably the most astonishing thing about parenthood is how truly fascinating it can be.

Note: You will find frequent use of "he," "his" and "him" as we discuss baby throughout these chapters. This in no way signifies any preference for boy babies. Rather it is in keeping with the common practice of referring to the male gender in order to avoid the clumsy "he-or-she." For the sake of novelty, however, we will occasionally substitute the female pronoun.

Not only is the newborn's appearance a temporary state, but also considering the surroundings from which he has just emerged, he probably doesn't look too bad at that.

Up to a generation ago, a newborn baby was thought to be little more than a warm lump that loosely resembled a miniature human body. In 1952 renowned child psychologist Jean Piaget, in *The Origins of Intelligence*, referred to the neonate as a small collection of "somewhat clumsy, unfinished and isolated reflexes." But research and observation of the newborn have shown that he might be more than that. Even before birth, the fetus exhibits sensitivity to light, sounds and temperature changes and has already been sucking its thumb for several weeks. In spite of a still incompletely organized nervous system, all the major organs are functioning.

Extensive physical development notwithstanding, a first glance at the typical newborn is likely to produce a slight sensation of shock. Parents unused to viewing newly arrived infants are apt to expect a dimpled, chortling, softly rounded bundle more nearly resembling a baby of five or six months. Instead they will more likely be presented with a wrinkled, puffy-faced, lumpy-headed, oddly-colored, crooked-shaped little creature—perhaps covered with fine dark hair (known as *lanugo*, which will disappear completely in a few months), and possibly still coated with *vernix*, a white, waxy material that has facilitated the newborn's passage through the birth canal. All, or nearly all, of the latter is usually removed during baby's first bath, shortly after birth. The rest will be absorbed by his skin within the next 24 hours. There may be small lesions on his wrists from prenatal sucking, and he may look slightly groggy from the effects of anesthesia.

Small wonder that so many parents question whether the infant is really their own! (You can be sure it is, because in almost every hospital in the country today, matching bracelets or ID tags are clamped to both mother and baby immediately after birth.) Before the disappointment becomes too overwhelming, however, keep in mind that not only is the newborn's appearance a temporary state, but also considering the surroundings from which he has just emerged, he probably doesn't look too bad at that!

At birth your baby will probably weigh somewhere between seven and eight pounds, but he could easily weigh either a little less or a little more than that. He will probably measure between 18 to 22 inches in length. The newborn's heart beats about 120 times a minute, and he breathes about 33 times in a minute. Both breathing and heartbeat rates are almost twice those of an adult. In baby they may vary considerably, depending on the individual baby and his state of excitement or activity.

Perhaps one of the more perplexing facets of the neonate's appearance is the peculiar shape of his disproportionately large head. The head comprises about one-fourth of his entire body length and, invariably, at the time of birth it is too large

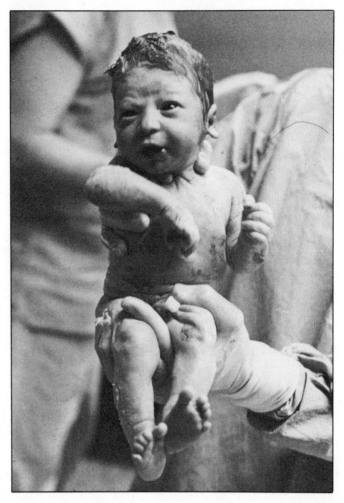

to be accommodated by the mother's birth canal. Nature has provided for this unusual state of affairs by allowing the infant's head to temporarily reshape itself. Before birth certain of the bones in the oversized skull overlap in such a way that the head size is decreased without any damage to the brain. This molding process is what often causes the infant's head to take on a melon-shaped appearance, slightly pointed in the back. Of course, the head returns to its normal shape within a few days after birth. A soft swelling of fluid on top of the head, known as a "caput succadaneum," may occur as a result of pressure from the pelvis during birth. It will disappear in a week or so.

Other peculiarities may include misshapen ears or other features temporarily pushed out of place during the birth process. Usually the legs are bowed, and the feet may be turned—sometimes in the same direction. The latter is often referred to as the "windblown effect" and is caused by the particular position of the feet in the uterus. Usually the feet straighten themselves within a week or so.

Often the skin of the newborn is loose and wrinkly, but within the first few days, it may begin to crack and peel, especially in the folds of the hands and feet. During these early days the Caucasian infant's color may range anywhere from purplish blue to pale pink or pinkish gray. Babies of Negro, Mediterranean or Asian heritage usually do not reveal their natural pigmentation for several hours or even

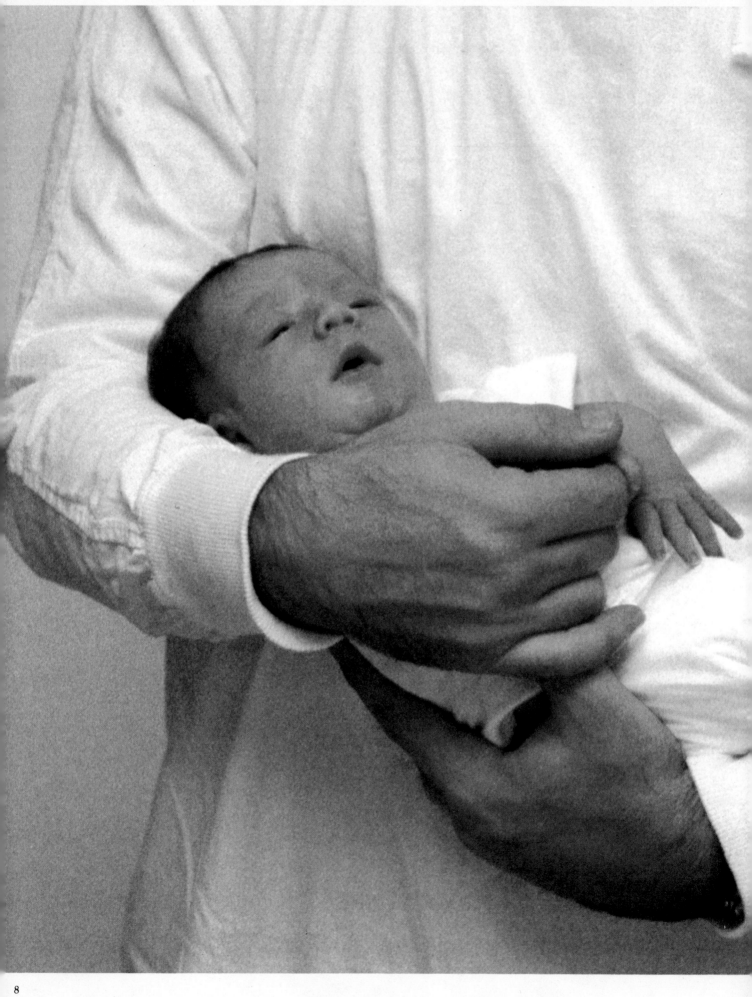

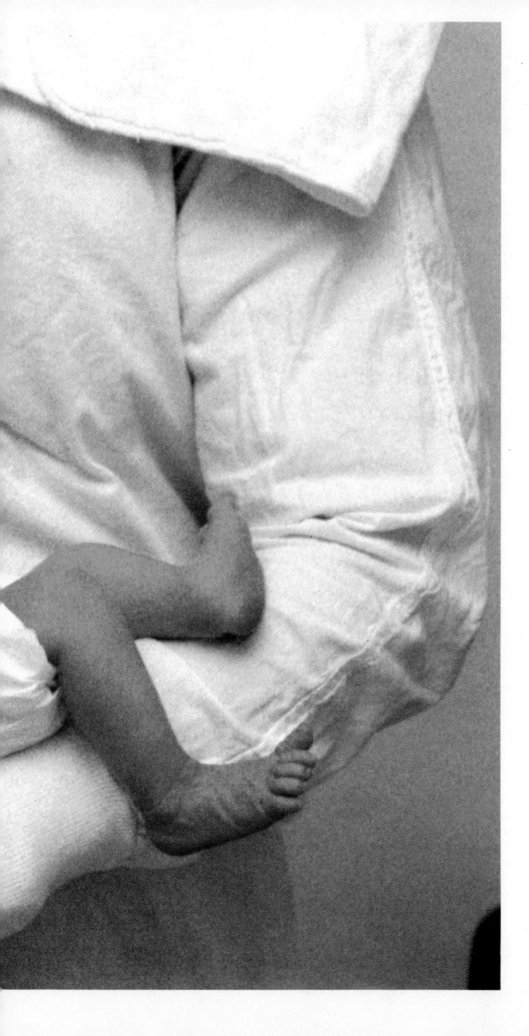

days. Many such babies are born with relatively light skin that later darkens somewhat. Among other things, frequent change in coloration of all babies is associated with temperature and activity fluctuations as well as changes occurring in the circulatory system.

A bluish color, or cyanosis, is often caused by the infant's efforts to expel remaining mucus from his air passages. Much of it is drained out at birth by holding the baby in an upside-down position. But there is still more material to be removed since the entire breathing apparatus has been totally filled with fluid up to the moment of birth. The newborn is most effectively equipped to rid himself of the unwanted mucus, however. A highly developed gag reflex prevents choking, and even though the infant appears to stop breathing and turns blue during a coughing seizure, there is no danger involved. A fear of brain damage due to temporary cessation of oxygen is unfounded—interestingly, the brain requires far less oxygen during the first few days than it will all the rest of its life since it has not yet completed the transition to an air-filled environment.

A yellow coloration during the third, fourth and fifth days is normal and is caused by a type of jaundice. While still in the uterus, with its relatively low oxygen supply, the fetus required many more red blood cells than it does after birth. The extra red cells are broken down by the infant, producing a yellow substance known as bilirubin. Bilirubin is normally excreted in the liver, but in the newborn that organ is not quite mature enough to rid the body of it as fast as it is produced; thus the yellow appearance of some babies, which may later change to a tan color. The color will fade by the time the infant is eight to ten days old.

Hemolytic jaundice is a more severe form of jaundice and is caused by an Rh negative moth-

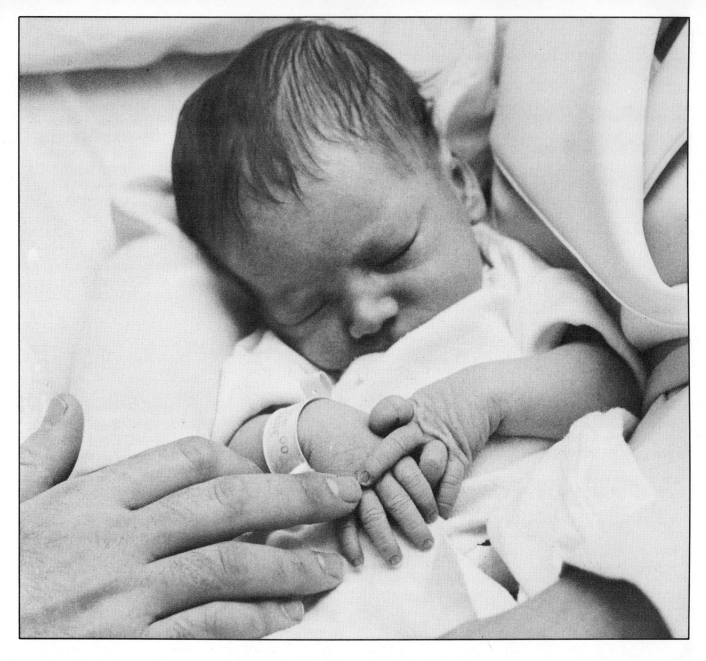

er giving birth to an Rh positive baby. Blood tests performed during pregnancy will already have alerted doctor and hospital staff to a possible incompatibility. Rarely is a first baby affected by the incompatible Rh factor since the mother will most likely have had no opportunity to build up the antibodies that could be harmful to her baby. Today drug treatment administered to the mother right after the birth of her first baby can prevent these antibodies from forming at all, thus protecting any babies she might have in the future.

If a newborn does develop hemolytic jaundice, the usual method of treatment is the use of a bilirubin lamp while baby is still in the hospital. Except for protection to his eyes, the infant is completely exposed to the light for several hours, or longer, until the excessive bilirubin in his blood has been destroyed. An affected baby may also be treated by an exchange transfusion.

Sometime after the first day or two, or anytime during the next few weeks, your baby may develop a harmless rash with the formidable name of erythematoxicum. Characteristically, the rash appears as a red blotch with a tiny, white, raised center, somewhat resembling heat rash. It doesn't usually affect the arms or legs but may occur on any other part of the body, sometimes appearing and disappearing before your eyes. The exact cause is unknown, but since it causes no discomfort and never lasts beyond the first few weeks, it is nothing to worry about.

Eyes may swell from a minor reaction to the silver nitrate drops administered immediately after birth. The rest of the face may show swollen spots if forceps were needed to assist the birth process. Because the circulation of the newborn is somewhat sluggish, actual forceps bruises may not appear for two or three days. Depressant effects on the baby caused by medication taken by the mother during labor, may continue as long as a week after birth—again as a result of an immature liver which is unable to clear the drugs from the body. While the infant may appear somewhat less alert than otherwise, there are no permanent effects.

A small blister on the upper lip from vigorous sucking is common with many babies. A dab of petroleum jelly will protect it.

We have mentioned some of the more common conditions that are present in the newborn, partly in the hope of allaying

10

some of your own fears as parents. But an additional factor is that even though you think you've just given birth to the most wonderful creature of the century, there is almost sure to be someone who is willing to point out some peculiarity or other. Comments and queries will range all the way from the possibility that one shoulder is higher than the other or one cheek plumper than the other, to why the fingers are wrinkled or one eye keeps closing. There may be embarrassed whisperings about the infant's enlarged breasts (due to hormones from the mother having crossed the placenta—a condition that will disappear in a few days), or if the child is a male, why he is already having erections (they are common, frequent, occur while awake or asleep and often in a series, and are probably caused by unaccustomed pressure from feces or a full bladder).

Why visitors to the new baby should feel compelled to immediately and thoroughly examine him for faulty workmanship is beyond the scope of this text. Nevertheless, the phenomenon is as ubiquitous as the presence of strange-looking babies and should be no cause for alarm. If you feel any doubt, check with your doctor. In the rare instance where there is real cause for concern, you will be so informed; otherwise, you can relax and know that your baby will very soon "recover."

Crying style is as varied among newborns as is everything else about him or her. Some emit long, lusty squalls; others tend to voice their complaints a bit less noisily but more frequently. There is no average, although there is a general tendency toward very abrupt starts and stops. One research study claimed to have proved that newborn boys cry more and sleep less than girls, but subsequent studies in that area failed to duplicate those results. (In any case, many mothers of girl babies already know that the original study couldn't possibly be valid.)

A condition peculiar to hospital nurseries and doctors' waiting rooms is the "crying circuit" that is frequently set into motion. Babies only 24 to 48 hours old will cry significantly more often, even when they hear only tapes of other babies crying, than if they are left quietly alone. Researchers have not yet determined the reason for this social crying. There is the possibility that it may reflect innate feelings of empathy since the sounds are associated with the infant's own cries of distress. Or it may be that the baby has already learned to link the sound of crying with unpleasant feelings. This is an intriguing area for further study.

A primary source of the newborn's discomfort is his still immature temperature regulators. This is particularly true during the earliest days, when crying is mistakenly thought to be due to hunger. Since a breast-feeding mother's milk does not normally "come in" before the fourth or fifth day, nature has provided ways for each infant to satisfactorily cope with his own hunger problem. Most newborns have ample stores of sugar, fat and fluid for interim sustenance. (For those who do not, it may be necessary to feed sugar-water during the waiting period.) Watching a bottle-fed baby during his first two or three days, you can readily see the newborn's frequent disinterest in eating. Often his feeding attempts are gagged up

along with mucus. The sucking instinct is in immediate evidence, but often the infant appears unable to swallow—a definite cause for concern to the novice mother. It need not be: the baby is simply not yet ready to eat. And when ready, he or she does not really have to be taught how.

Sleep patterns have given rise to extensive research over the years. In 1940 Dr. Arnold Gesell of the famed Gesell Institute described the neonate as "quasi-dormant," existing in a "twilight zone between sleeping and waking." Research of the seventies, however, indicates that there are awake and asleep states, and that the newborn is awake far more of the time than was previously realized. Sleep states during the 24-hour period vary between deep sleep, light sleep, drowsiness, and wide-awake and visually alert. In some babies the different states are very definite while in others they may be indistinct enough so that it's difficult to tell whether baby is awake or asleep. Additionally, the infant may be found in a drowsy, transitional state for an hour or two each day.

During the time the newborn is awake, his crying doesn't automatically signify hunger. It could mean that he is uncomfortable, or it could be for reasons that we simply don't understand yet. His immature nervous system, still becoming accustomed to its new environment, probably needs comforting. Sensitive to the assaults of heat and cold, he may need swaddling or some of his covering removed. Most assuredly, you will know from his behavior whether or not he is pleased with the service.

The strange movements of the newborn—or sometimes the lack of them—often create concern. The jerky startle reactions can be most puzzling to those unfamiliar with them. Research shows that startles occur approximately every two or three minutes, particularly during periods of "quiet" sleep. The entire body quivers, arms extend up and out, and the head and trunk tend to bend forward.

Startle behavior is not the same as another common type of movement known as the Moro reflex. In the latter the arms also extend outward but are quickly flung back close to the chest. (Theory has it that such maneuvers are reminiscent of the climbing activity of our so-called ape ancestry.) All of these and similar spontaneous movements tend to taper off within the first two months, at least some of them probably becoming incorporated into the baby's awake behavior. In the early days, however, the unsteady nervous system sometimes sets up a vicious cycle: crying may cause the infant to startle, and in turn the startle causes the baby to cry. Often the only way the chain can be broken is by firmly grasping a part of baby's body—an arm or leg, for example—to settle him down.

The stepping reflex is another example of instinctive behavior. If the infant is gently held in a standing position and one foot at a time gently pressed down against the crib, she will lift each foot in turn as though trying to walk. This is an excellent example of a reflex that gradually diminishes and then reappears later as a voluntary, controlled action.

The newborn often sleeps in the classic fetal position—arms drawn in close to the chest, knees bent and pulled up close to the abdomen. These flexed positions contrast strangely with occasional semi- frogleg extensions. The head is turned

11

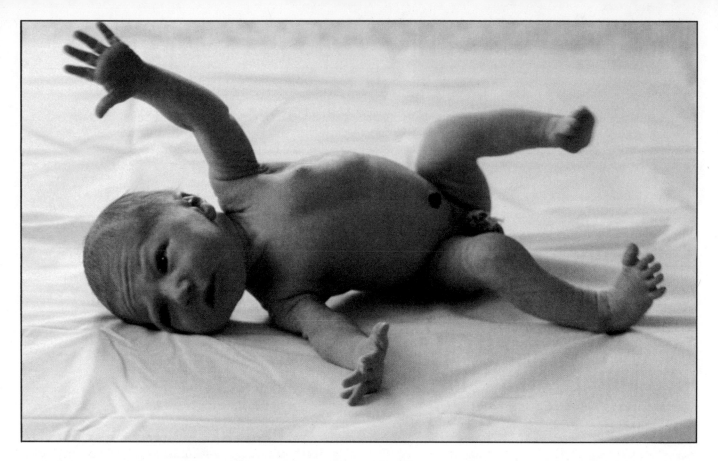

easily from side to side. The nose twitches, and the mouth forms itself incessantly into every sort of shape. Kicking and flailing of the arms may be almost too enthusiastic—or almost nonexistent. A quiet baby frequently appears almost completely relaxed; a very active one as though he can hardly wait to walk off and pursue the business of living.

Even a newborn will make grasping motions, but here again this is a reflex action and not any conscious effort to hold something in the hand. Grasping will have decreased noticeably by the end of ten days and then will reappear several weeks later as baby willfully begins to examine objects of interest.

A rudimentary grasping reflex also affects a baby's feet. Known as the Babinski reflex, it occurs when the soles of the feet are stroked. The feet will bend upward, the toes fan out, and the big toes lift higher than the others.

Even a newborn makes instinctive attempts to protect himself. If his face is covered with a cloth or blanket, he will flail with his arms and twist his head back and forth to remove the covering. His maneuvers may be primitive, but they are determined enough to make accidental smothering almost an impossibility. Likewise, baby will quickly withdraw from a pinch or pinprick. If an arm or leg is exposed to cold air, he will pull the limb in close to him in an effort to warm it.

Practically universal among newborns is the ability to connect fist with mouth. When newborns actually suck their thumbs, the probability is strong that the thumb found its way there by accident. But baby's mouthing of fingers or entire fist is common and can be initiated by stroking either the mouth or the hand. The rooting reflex is equally strong—that is, the infant's turning his head toward a particular stimulus such as a soft stroking of his cheek. In fact, this reflex is so strong that test studies have utilized it in

determining a newborn's ability to memorize and learn. It has been discovered that infants as young as two days old can be taught to turn their heads to a designated side. They don't really know what they're looking for just yet, but they know when they have found it.

The rooting reflex, together with the sucking reflex, is necessary to the infant's survival; without them he would have difficulty learning to eat. If necessary, the sucking reflex may need to be stimulated at first by gently stroking the soft palate. The newborn's sense of smell is probably developed enough to assist in food-finding expeditions. The likelihood is that his abilities to see and hear are so much better developed than the smell instinct that it often goes unnoticed. Chances are that sense of smell also plays a far greater role among adults than is commonly realized; one theory suggests that it may be instrumental in establishing certain positive or negative relationships between individuals.

As enjoyable and comforting as sucking behavior is to babies of almost every age, even a newborn will stop sucking to regard other stimuli. In general, infants will cease sucking to listen to a new sound. A loud or unpleasant noise doesn't necessarily elicit this same type of behavior. Instead, it seems to be more than the infant is able to cope with, so the tendency is to shut it out by promptly falling asleep.

Visual stimuli evoke similar cessation of sucking and, as with sound, excessive amounts will put baby to sleep. Yes, newborns most definitely *can* see but only within a limited field. They don't see as well as they hear but immediately after birth will blink at a bright light. They see best the objects that are about eight inches away—one explanation for their early interest in and acquaintance with mother's face. While studies indicate that newborns do perceive in three dimensions, they probably are not able to see in color before the age of four or five months. For a while research suggested that even newborns could distinguish colors, but further testing demonstrated that what the infants were really distinguishing was the difference in degree of *brightness* of the colors. From the earliest days babies are also able to differentiate various patterns and shapes.

Up to the early 1960s, it was generally believed by pediatricians that a baby could see practically nothing during his first six weeks. Intuitive mothers the world over insisted otherwise, certain that the intensity with which a baby stared at his mother's face obviously meant he could see. The newborn, however, probably won't glance in the direction of the face very often and probably won't dwell on his mother's eyes at all in the first week or two.

Mothers do not always correctly "know" their baby's responses. Many are sure that the infant smiles at them periodically. Through repeated studies scientists know that a baby cannot exhibit purposeful smiling before he is a few weeks old. As the newborn continually experiments with his complex set of facial muscles, inevitably he will occasionally produce a smile. The difference is that it simply is not a true social smile. (When the first of those occurs, you will know. Baby seems to smile with his entire body!)

We assume that during the latter part of your pregnancy, you arranged for a doctor to care for your baby. As soon as possible after birth, you or your obstetrician should contact your chosen doctor or pediatrician. He or she will then be able to perform a very thorough examination of your baby while still in the hospital. Obviously, if baby requires any kind of special attention, it should be begun as soon as possible. If you do not already have a pediatrician available, ask your obstetrician to recommend someone.

Your pediatrician is invaluable in helping you and your baby get off to a good start. He will advise you about feeding and general care and will answer any questions you might have. (And you probably have a number of them.) He will also set up an immunization schedule for your baby that will continue at least through her first year, plus the necessary booster shots thereafter. During baby's first few months, he will receive a series of DTP shots (for diphtheria, pertussis or whooping cough, and tetanus) and a series of polio vaccine. In later months he will be inoculated against measles, rubella (German measles) and probably mumps.

These immunizations are immensely important for your baby and must not be neglected. Try to never miss a monthly appointment with your pediatrician. You don't want the series of shots to be interrupted. (If you feel you're financially unable

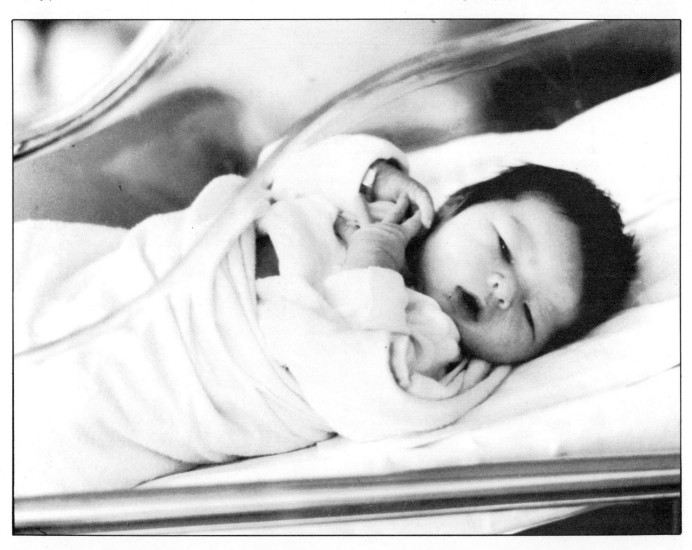

to afford all of the necessary shots through a private physician, check with your local health department. They will tell you how to arrange for them free.)

But while you're concerning yourself with feeding and bathing and diapers and shots, don't become so involved that you forget the one thing your baby needs most of all: *you*. He needs your warmth and your cuddling. He needs to be close to those body noises and movements that had become familiar to him before birth.

In *How to Parent*, Dr. Fitzhugh Dodson discusses a study conducted by Dr. Harry Harlow in which baby rhesus monkeys were raised by terry-cloth dummies that had built-in nursing bottles. The monkeys received sufficient nourishment but not sufficient amounts of what Dr. Harlow refers to as "contact comfort," since no adult monkeys were available to demonstrate physical affection. All of the monkeys grew into socially inadequate adults, "unable to mate with receptive monkeys of the opposite sex, and they showed strange and weird mannerisms, much like those observed in human psychotics."

Of course, we don't mean to imply that your new baby in any way resembles a baby rhesus monkey! (But neither would we suggest that such a study be performed on human babies.) Until fairly recently the importance of physical contact between mother and baby had been grossly underestimated, and many parents feared that too much cuddling would encourage overdependence. Precisely the opposite is true: independence grows out of security. Babies love to be carried in an upright position, for example, molding close to the parent's body. The motion and physical contact are both soothing and stimulating. Don't be afraid to let your baby know how much you love him.

Everything about a newborn is more subtle than it will be a few weeks from now. By the end of your baby's first week, you will already notice small changes. His physical appearance will have changed; he will have regained some of the weight lost during the first few days, and much of the "lumpiness" and other peculiarities will have begun to disappear. As you cuddle, rock or talk to him, you will notice some very individual responses to you in addition to the obvious soothing effects of your efforts. Probably he is already letting you know exactly how he prefers to be held at feeding time or during quiet times.

Subtle as the changes may be, they represent an almost continual state of transition. It is useless to assume that such rapid development can fit into a rigid schedule. You will want to channel baby's daily timetable toward one that will more or less coincide with your own, but keep in mind that the infant is simply not equipped to deal with ultimatums. For your own well-being, keep flexible; arrange for temporary help at home, if possible; get enough rest—which will mean a daytime nap to make up for those middle-of-the-night sojourns.

Above all, try not to worry. The neighbors won't mind if you don't vacuum your living room or make your bed for a few days. (If anyone besides you *does* mind, he or she can be invited to perform the chore for you.) As we have already tried to point out, your baby isn't judging you. You are allowed to make a mistake or an ill-conceived decision. Your baby will continue to grow and develop in spite of your mistakes or lack of knowledge. Relax—and you're off to a rewarding start in your new endeavor.

development chart

PHYSICAL	SENSORYMOTOR	INTELLECTUAL	SOCIAL
Total body responds to sudden changes. Arm, leg and hand movements controlled primarily by reflexes. Lies in froglike position or rolled into ball when on stomach. Moves head side to side. Can lift head when held on adult's shoulder. Head flops forward or back when pulled to sitting position. Swallowing and rooting controlled by reflex. Moves bowels often and sporadically. Sleeps 70-80% of day in 7-8 daily naps. Requires 7-8 feedings a day.	Blinks at bright light. Sees light and dark patterns. Focuses about 8" away. Sensitive to location of sound. Distinguishes volume and pitch of sound; tends to prefer high-toned voices. Grips object if hand strikes it accidentally. Reflex grasp causes hands to remain fisted much of time. Eyes tend to turn outward.	Quiets when picked up or in response to any firm, steady pressure. Sleeping, waking on a continuum. Stops sucking to look at something. Shuts out disturbing stimuli by lapsing into sleep.	Shows excitement, distress. Becomes alert to and tries to focus on face or voice. Appears to respond positively to soft sounds of human voice. Is individual in looks, feelings, activity level and reaction to stimulation.

Note: These charts are to be regarded as guidelines only. Many babies will perform each activity earlier or later than indicated.

Baby enjoys watching the human face, particularly her mother's, since that is the one which is most familiar.

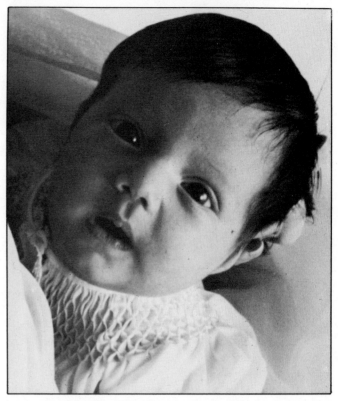

Just as you have begun to suspect that your new baby really belonged to the hospital instead of you and your husband, it's homecoming time. If you're a new mother, you're probably thrilled, impatient and more than a little frightened. Your anticipated happiness at being home again may be dulled a bit almost as soon as you walk through the front door: where did all the dust come from, and how could one person collect such a mountain of dirty dishes?

But you are determined not to worry about such insignificant matters and concentrate instead on settling baby into his new quarters. Most likely you will either have too much help or not enough, and so begin the problems. These problems, however, are not insurmountable and not forever. You should try to arrange for one person (or one set of grandparents) to remain with you, and strongly encourage everyone else to leave after a short visit. If you cannot afford to hire a live-in baby nurse for the first week or two and are unable to arrange for a relative or friend to stay at your home, then at the very least try to hire a helper who is experienced with newborns.

Inevitably, a new baby in the family creates a need for major readjustments. A first-time mother struggles with an overwhelming number of things she's trying to remember. Father may well feel somewhat rejected, unneeded and almost certainly helpless. Grandmothers may try to "take over" and cause feelings of resentment all around. An older sibling will exhibit mingled feelings of curiosity, jealousy and pride. And baby himself, still trying to adjust to his new world, must now become accustomed to different surroundings and routines. If, in addition, neighbors, friends and other relatives are rushing in and out, each offering advice on how to quiet baby's howls, the result can be total chaos.

Keep visitors to a minimum during those early days or for as long as possible. Make every attempt to ward off the deluge of unsolicited advice you are sure to receive. ("That sounds like a good idea but my doctor says..." is a tactful rejoinder that usually works.) And while you yourself may be filled with fears, concerns and questions, don't let them overpower you. Check with your doctor or another person in whom you have confidence. Any deviation from what new parents perceive as normal sets off a flurry of overconcern. As we have mentioned before, there is no average baby. Each will display his own patterns of eating, sleeping, crying and movement. And that set of patterns is almost sure to be different from those of your recently born niece or the baby next door.

During the next three weeks your baby's appearance will begin to change. As the 12 tiny eyeball muscles come under increasing control, his vision will become more fixed, although his eyes may still look crossed or wall-eyed at times. Activity rate increases, becoming more rhythmic and more intense. Moods develop. Already the barest hints of future personality traits may begin to emerge: one baby may be very active and noisy while another appears more contented and quiet. All will gradually display a greater awareness of what is going on around them.

By mid-month most babies will have set themselves on a more or less regular feeding schedule, but don't count on it. Somewhere around the end of the month, baby will be ready to give up his middle-of-the-night bottle or breast, although he probably won't sleep much more than six hours at a stretch. While you'll want to encourage this long sleep period to come at night rather than during the day, there is otherwise little reason to adhere to any rigid feeding schedule. Four-hour schedules and demand feeding have all had their heyday as the only "right" way to feed an infant. Finally, experts today are in almost unanimous agreement that the logical method is to feed baby when he's hungry.

The term "demand" is an unfortunate one, conjuring up visions of a raging tyrant commanding his mother to do his bidding and on-the-double. For many years theory had it that a demand feeder would eventually grow into a disagreeable, uncontrollable child interested only in his own gratification. Nonsense! The infant mind is completely incapable of engineering such a complex plot. He has no desire to beat his caretaker into humble submission; he only knows that he is hungry. His immature nervous system is not connected to an alarm clock, and if left in misery until it's "time" to be hungry, he can only deduce he has entered a mighty peculiar and unpleasant world.

Until your baby is ready to give up that first middle-of-the-night bottle, she may wake several times during the night. Sleep states still vary from light to deep sleep, and during waking hours your baby may be actively awake or quiet or crying. A few babies remain awake as many as 12 hours out of the 24, but their eyes will be closed during part of that time.

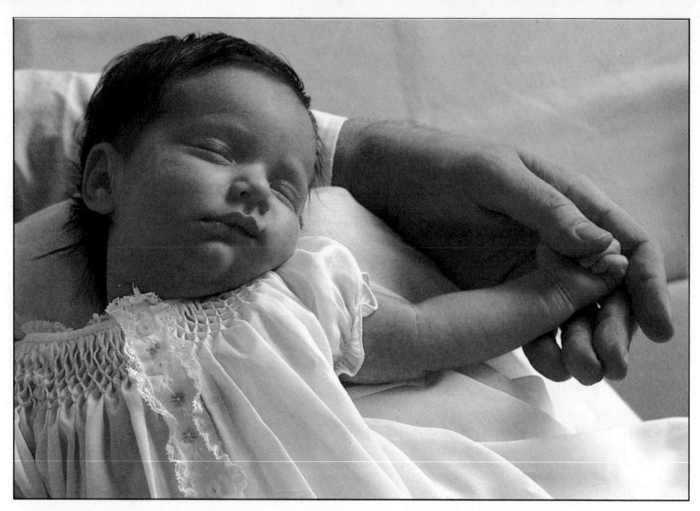

During the first month the tonic neck reflex (TNR) becomes established. This characteristic position of all babies generally continues until about twelve weeks. When lying on his back, the infant turns his head to a preferred side; the arm on the same side of the body is extended, and the opposite arm is bent, with the hand somewhere near the head or chest. Thus the reason this reflex is also referred to as the "fencer's pose."

In early infancy babies are protected from an onslaught to their nervous systems by what scientists refer to as the stimulus barrier. The sudden bombardment by every sort of sight, sound and smell as baby enters his new world is more than he can accommodate at one time. Thus he first focuses his attention on a few low-key stimuli and merely shuts out what he is unable to handle. This is a major reason why it is unnecessary to keep your living quarters in absolute quiet while baby sleeps. Doing so will only accustom him to silence.

The startle-and-cry reflex is still in evidence; i.e., your baby will generally react with a jerk and a scream to a sudden loud noise, bright light, jolt or quick change of position. But following this initial reaction, he will then simply close his eyes against continued strong light, for example, and will appear oblivious to prolonged harsh noise, perhaps even falling asleep. You may feel that baby is only pretending to be asleep, but electroencephalograph studies with new babies under such conditions reveal brain-wave patterns that are identical to those that occur during ordinary sleep. Conversely, baby will react with curiosity to soft whispering in his ear, turning toward the sound as though to examine its source. During the coming weeks, more and more stimuli will be added to your baby's repertoire, and much of his "withdrawn" behavior will gradually diminish.

Rooting and sucking instincts are still very strong. Your baby no longer spends precious seconds having to hunt for the nipple and can get right down to the business of eating. A breast-feeding baby will balk if his mother offers him a bottle instead and will probably convince her that he'd rather starve. However, he may accept a bottle fairly willingly from his father or other caretaker *if* his mother is not in the same room. She may be out of his range of vision, but if she's near enough, he may recognize her smell and the sounds of her voice and her footsteps.

The baby's field of vision is limited considerably by the tonic neck reflex. Although she can turn her head to follow a moving object, it doesn't occur to her to do so: once the object is out of sight, to baby's mind it has disappeared. She is contented to gaze at patterns or designs for long periods of time, possibly indicating a preference for these over solidly colored areas. The patterns can be black and white since baby will not see color for several weeks yet, but they should be close enough during these early weeks so that she is able to focus on them easily. Distance will vary according to size; a little experimenting will quickly tell you whether your baby is looking at the objects, posters, mobiles, patches of sunlight or whatever patterned items you and Mother Nature have provided.

Baby also enjoys watching the human face, particularly his mother's since hers is usually the one that is most familiar. (Authorities disagree somewhat on whether babies prefer faces to patterned designs, but it seems only humanistic to assume they would prefer faces.) Baby will intently study the entire face, tending at first to focus on just one or two features. The chosen features are usually those toward the edge of the face, such as an ear or the chin, but some infants prefer the eyes.

By the end of the first month, your baby may try to respond to the voices he has been hearing by venturing a few "almost" gurgles and coos. Don't be surprised, however, if his vocalizing is still limited to little throat noises—it's early yet.

Your baby can easily be made to grasp an adult's finger. During the early weeks baby's hands are at least partly closed most of the time. When touched, they will either open or clench in reflex action; if they open, a second touch will cause them to close around the probing finger. Reminiscent of our primitive ancestry, baby's feet also exhibit a grasping tendency.

Still another reflex that probably has more interest value than practical application, is what is known as the "doll's eye" effect. When a baby who is lying down with closed eyes is lifted upright, her eyes will open wide. It is difficult to avoid noticing her resemblance to a toy doll that has weights on the backs of its eyes to make them open and close.

Although your baby is still very young and much of his behavior is governed by instinct, it is not too early to begin gently and slowly providing appropriate forms of stimulation. You will furnish much of it at feeding time: taste, touch, smell, vision, motion and voice. He won't reply but nevertheless enjoys listening as you talk and sing to him at any time he is awake. See that he has interesting things to look at from his crib. Because baby's head is so often turned to the side due to the tonic neck reflex, small mobiles or brightly patterned toys dangling at the sides of his crib will be more likely to rouse his interest than those that hang overhead. You can make simple ones yourself from whatever you happen to have around the house—bright plastic or foil Christmas ornaments, for example.

Don't overdo the stimulation you offer baby. It isn't necessary, or desirable, to entertain him throughout his waking hours. But do remember that he is already learning, and he cannot learn efficiently without the "food" to stir his senses.

By the end of the month, you may encounter the joy of your baby's first real smile. It usually appears between the third and sixth weeks, and you'll recognize it as being different from the early "pre-smiles" because this time baby's eyes crinkle, and his entire face seems to be involved.

From birth the corners of his mouth will have turned up occasionally, almost as though he were experimenting. Most often these expressions occur when baby is drowsy or sleeping and are usually accompanied by rapid eye movements. By the second week baby begins to respond slightly to the relatively high-pitched sounds of the female voice. As he reaches toward the outer world, he may sometimes present an amusing expression resembling a "drunken" smile. The muscles are not quite under control yet. But sometime after the third week, you will witness an alert, open-eyed, true smile.

Don't feel you must constantly smile at your baby so that he will "learn" how to make his own. Blind infants begin to smile at exactly the same ages, indicating that the strongest stimuli are a mother's voice and touch.

There are a myriad of things for new parents to worry about. We will mention here a few of the more common ones, but first a word of caution: if you have any doubts, call your

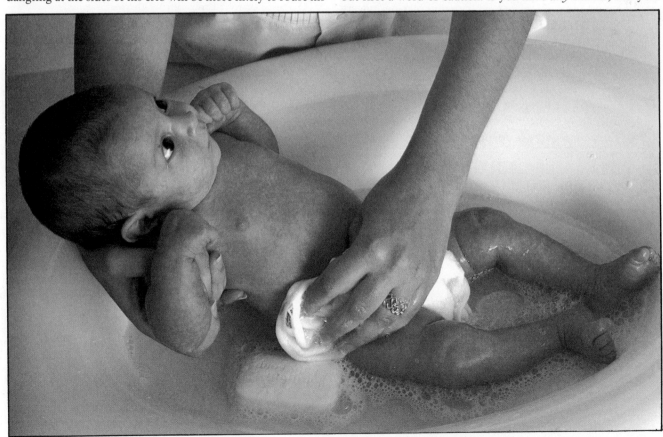

doctor. Don't worry that your questions may sound silly; you can be sure that pediatricians everywhere, and their nurses, have probably heard the same questions many times before.

Before you left the hospital, a nurse or doctor will have told you how to care for your baby's circumcision (if you have a boy) and the stump of the umbilical cord. The cord normally falls off about the beginning of the second week, but a few babies do not lose it before the end of three weeks. Usually you will be instructed not to begin tub baths until the cord stump is off. A dab of petroleum jelly will prevent diapers from sticking to either the cord or circumcised area if that should be a problem.

Swollen breasts may persist in babies of either sex, possibly accompanied by a slight, milky discharge. Girl babies may have a trace of bleeding from the vagina. Both conditions will disappear as soon as the remaining hormones from the mother are completely eliminated from the baby's body. Neither should be a cause of concern.

Occasionally a blocked tear duct may cause one eye to drain tears while preventing the baby from blinking away dust. This is not a serious condition, but your doctor should be consulted. He or she will advise you how to bathe the eye with sterile water and to massage away the excess tears. Usually the massage itself will open the blocked duct; if not, it is a simple procedure for the doctor to do in his office.

You may notice various tiny scratches on your baby's face or other parts of her body. That means it's time to cut her fingernails, best done while she's sleeping, using a pair of *blunt*-tipped nail scissors. Cut them straight across and not too close. The process will have to be repeated frequently until the baby has better control of her hand movements. In the hospital scratching may have been prevented by hand coverings. At home this is neither necessary nor advisable. Baby needs the opportunity to look at her hands and suck her fingers.

Small, deep pink or red spots on baby's forehead, eyelids or the back of his neck are rarely permanent. Known as "stork bites" they may be present at birth or may not appear until between one and four weeks. They're caused by tiny capillary blood vessels close to the surface of baby's almost transparent skin and usually grow brighter when he's crying, becoming paler again (sometimes to just a pale pink) when he is quieted. They almost always disappear completely by the age of three or four years.

The anterior fontanel, or "soft spot," on the top of your baby's head has given rise to more than its share of baby-care myths. Contrary to what you may have heard, there is no danger in touching or washing it just as you do the rest of your baby's head. The fontanel allows the baby's rapidly growing brain to expand as necessary, a feat that the slower-growing skull bones could not permit. In addition, the soft spot provides a cushion to protect against possible blows to the head. Without this protection a head injury could easily result in concussion, just as it does in an adult. The spot will close at about the age of 18 months, when the period of most rapid brain growth has ended and baby is no longer so prone to falling on his head.

Many very young babies do a lot of sneezing and sniffling because the hairs of the nose are not sufficiently developed to keep the nasal passages free from mucus. If this is a problem, gently clean the area with a damp washcloth. If the nose tends to become crusty, smear a tiny amount of petroleum jelly near the nasal openings (but don't put it *in* the nose).

A small blister on the upper lip from vigorous sucking is common with many babies. Again, a dab of petroleum jelly will protect it.

Baby's bowel movements are a frequent source of concern for new parents because the color and consistency seem so unusual. Consider how different a baby's diet is from your own. In later months, as solid foods are added, baby's b.m.s will begin to more nearly resemble those of an adult. During the first week or two of life, however, the stools are composed of a sticky, greenish black substance known as meconium. Gradually the stools will become lighter and less sticky as the first true bowel movements begin. Color will vary considerably for each baby, depending partly on whether he is being breast- or bottle-fed. Those of the breast-fed baby will be light yellow to yellow-orange; the color for the bottle-fed baby will tend to be more brownish or clay-colored. All babies may occasionally have stools that are partly green (due to bile that has not yet changed color) or containing curds (from undigested milk). Consistency will vary from relatively firm to soft and almost watery, like loose scrambled eggs. You will quickly learn what is usual for your baby.

All babies spit up occasionally after eating, but some, particularly the more active ones, spit up what appear to be enormous amounts after every feeding. This is more a nuisance than any real cause for concern. As long as your baby continues to gain weight regularly, you will know she is keeping down a sufficient portion of each meal. It may help to prop her in a semi-sitting position for a half-hour after each feeding; but then again it may not. Try encouraging baby to suck more slowly, perhaps using nipples with smaller holes. If she will allow it (some babies won't!), you can try burping her three or four times during the feeding.

Crying is inevitable in all babies. Until speech is fairly well developed, baby's life seems to be peppered with numerous fussy periods that may seem unexplainable. Sometime during the last half of the first month, most will have established regular bouts of irritable crying—commonly occurring in the evening or approaching the dinner hour, when household tensions tend to be at a peak. Science has yet to discover all of the reasons for this periodic crying or why in some babies it reaches an intensity and frequency that qualify it as colic.

Generally a baby's irritable crying can be considered colic when it is loud and screaming, regularly lasts as long as from one feeding to the next, and stops as suddenly as it starts. The baby is obviously miserable, and nothing seems to comfort him. A certain amount of gas is usually expelled during these crying bouts—a clue to the fact that he is probably suffering from an old-fashioned stomach ache. The only good thing that can be said about colic is that it disappears almost entirely by the end of the third month.

It may be little salvation to harried new parents to say "Relax!"—yet that is probably the single most important means of calming the household. You may need to remind yourself frequently that the colic will be over in a few weeks. It may help, too, if you realize that, almost without exception, colicky babies are extremely healthy and alert little beings.

We offer here a few suggestions that might soothe your

baby, at least to some degree. Don't try them all at once. Have enough patience to give each a chance to work, and remember that different "solutions" may be more effective on different days or different times of the day.

Most obvious, of course, is holding and perhaps gently rocking your baby. Sometimes swaddling him snugly in a receiving blanket will help, but some babies only feel too restrained and become more angry. Talk or sing to him softly. Keep all your movements slow; don't jiggle and bounce or feel you have to keep up a nonstop patter.

While we have said that a crying baby should be tended as quickly as possible and not left alone in his crib for long periods, we did not intend to imply a lack of common sense. If your baby has just eaten and cuddling doesn't quiet him after a reasonable length of time, there's no need to feel guilty about returning him to his crib. If you're feeling particularly nervous or tense, you'll probably both be better off with this solution. Do try bubbling him first, however, and continue it intermittently throughout the entire crying period. A howling baby swallows air, which only adds to his problem.

You may wish to try filling a hot-water bottle (with *warm* water), wrapping it in a towel and holding it on baby's stomach. A baby almost always enjoys the comforting warmth.

There are now on the market records and tapes of the heartbeats and womb sounds of pregnancy. Many fretting babies are calmed by these familiar sounds; soft music playing nearby can be just as effective.

Unless you are strongly opposed, a pacifier can be a useful device in soothing baby. In early infancy it often provides greater sucking satisfaction than a thumb that cannot easily find its way into baby's mouth. A great many babies require more sucking time than feeding periods allow, and this is a classic form of relaxation for a baby.

A few babies, even in these earliest weeks, appear to suffer from boredom. Some mothers have successfully handled the crying problem by placing baby in his infant seat or carrier and moving him about the house with her. Placed in a semi sitting or upright position, he has a new view of his surroundings. Even though his eyes can't make out too much just yet, he can hear his mother's voice and footsteps and may find contentment in visually exploring within his limited range. It is possible, too, that the semi-upright position may relieve pressure on his digestive system from unexpelled gas.

As interaction continues to develop, both parent and child learn the means—or at least how to respond—to different voice inflection or facial expression. Your baby has his own set of characteristics that make him special. A bit of interested attention will enable you to become aware of some of his unique interests, needs, desires, and dislikes. As an illustration of how finely tuned this pre speech communicating can become, various studies have been performed with blind infants. Although unnoticed by adults without special training, researchers discovered that these babies and their mothers possessed a sort of hand language in lieu of the usual signs and signals utilized by young babies. Communication thrived!

Colic, or fussy crying in any amount, can seem overwhelming at times. We remind you again that it is a very temporary

state. When baby's first smile comes along, you'll know for sure that sunnier days are ahead. During his second month there will be still other new accomplishments to mutually enjoy with your baby. And gradually you and baby are learning to interpret each other's movements, gestures and sounds to create what Louise J. Kaplan refers to in *Oneness and Separateness* as "early dialogue."

The phenomenon known as the postpartum blues is quite common in our culture. It occurs in varying degrees, sometimes as only infrequent, mild attacks; sometimes serious enough to require medical assistance. Most often it occurs after the birth of the first child, but there are no limitations. It may begin as a post-delivery letdown while a mother is still in the hospital, or it may not start until several weeks later when she feels that life should have settled down into something more nearly resembling a normal routine.

What exactly is postpartum depression and what causes it? Probably the simplest answer is that it's a combination of disappointment and fatigue. No matter how well-prepared you may have been about your newborn's physical appearance, you may still have secretly felt a touch of uneasiness that he didn't look just a wee bit more like the babies on television commercials. After three or four weeks, you may feel you've already donated enough sleepless nights to the cause, and baby ought to be gracious enough to stop waking up at night. Then when baby begins to stay awake for longer periods, life may seem to take on a merry-go-round tempo with its exhausting and seemingly endless cycle of feeding, burping, changing,

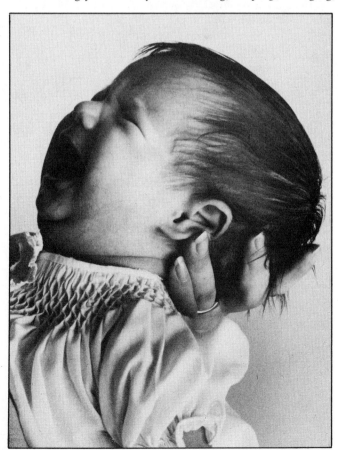

bathing, rocking, soothing, cleaning, shopping, washing and cooking. There never seems to be enough time for you or your husband. Even an invitation to a special social event doesn't interest you: you'd rather sleep. You may feel confused and helpless. On the other hand, you may have given birth to what is generally referred to as a quiet baby—one who is so little problem that you feel unfulfilled, unneeded, as though there were really nothing to do.

The result is the same: You cannot help asking, "Is this all there is to it?"

Psychologists have ventured the opinion that the very helplessness of a baby stimulates a mother's need for mothering. That is probably true to an extent, but when you're exhausted and feeling out of touch with the rest of the world, you probably aren't going to feel motherly all the time. At least occasionally you'll feel resentful; that in turn will probably cause you to feel guilty. You may question your ability as a parent and wonder what's wrong with you.

First of all, there is probably nothing wrong with *you*; you are simply enduring the adjustment pangs of motherhood. As with any new endeavor, it will take some time. And you're bound to feel displeased at least once in a while.

Can postpartum depression be prevented? Perhaps not entirely, but there are ways to minimize it. The single most important blues-chaser is adequate rest. No one can cope with even minor problems through a haze of perpetual fatigue. You will need some kind of help. After the first week or two, you may not be able to afford or have available full-time help. But do make every effort to have some kind of part-time help, either with the baby or with the housework.

Don't allow your baby to completely dominate your life. It is neither necessary nor desirable to spend *all* your time engrossed in baby care. Save some time for your husband and, particularly, save some time for yourself. Try to set aside at least half an hour a day to do something just for yourself. At the same time don't exhaust yourself further by trying to resume your entire pre-baby social regimen.

As new parents, you are still a couple. Keep the lines of communication open. Tell each other how you feel. A wife must understand that her husband may find it difficult to refrain from feeling jealous and neglected at times; a husband must try to be patient when his wife dissolves into tears for no apparent reason or displays an unreasonable fit of temper. Sensitivities come into play on both sides and must be dealt with sensibly. (There is no logic in each blaming the other because the baby is crying, for instance.)

Talking with other new mothers often affords a release for some of these new tensions. Many women are able to relax more in simply knowing they are not alone in what they have feared are "peculiar" or "wrong" reactions to motherhood. If, however, you continue to feel severely overwhelmed and depressed for long periods; if you find yourself less and less able to carry out the simplest daily tasks; if your closest friends are telling you that you're not yourself—then you may be in need of professional help. Don't hesitate or feel embarrassed about calling your doctor. Postpartum blues is a condition well-known in the medical field, and your physician will be able to suggest professional counseling.

A particular area of conflict to new parents often arises after the mother's post delivery medical checkup, when she is given the go-ahead to resume sexual activities. She may feel too distraught or exhausted to even show any interest. It almost goes without saying that such reactions may be extremely upsetting to her; most certainly they will be upsetting to her husband.

Again, talk it out. Look for possible solutions, and keep in mind that a few more weeks will bring the relief of more sleep, a greater sense of competency as parents and a great deal of mutual satisfaction in watching the development of your baby.

development chart

PHYSICAL	SENSORYMOTOR	INTELLECTUAL	SOCIAL
Arm, leg and hand movements are still primarily reflexive. Thrusts out arms and legs in play. Rolls part way to side from back. Lifts head briefly. May hold head in line with back when pulled to sit. Startles spontaneously (Moro reflex). Usually keeps hands fisted or slightly open. Moves bowels 3-4 times a day. Requires 2 night feedings plus 5 or 6 during the day.	Stares at object; doesn't reach for it. Coordinates eyes sideways in regarding light or object. Reflexes becoming more efficient. When fingers are pried open, grasps rattle or other object but drops it quickly. Indicates response to human voice. Roots at breast (even if not breast-feeding). Responds positively to comfort and satisfaction, negatively to pain.	Alert about one out of every ten hours. Vague, indirect and impassive regard and expression during most of waking hours. Remembers object that reappears within 2½ seconds. Expects feedings at certain intervals. Cries deliberately for assistance. Quiets at being held or seeing faces.	Most reactions still in response to inner stimuli. Eyes fix on mother's face in response to her smile if she's not too far away. Makes eye-to-eye contact. Stares at faces and responds by quieting. Adjusts posture to body of person holding him; may clutch at person. Daily patterns of sleeping, crying and eating are very disorganized.

Note: These charts are to be regarded as guidelines only. Many babies will perform each activity earlier or later than indicated.

In addition to preferring that her head be turned to a particular side, baby will also exhibit definite preferences in sleeping position.

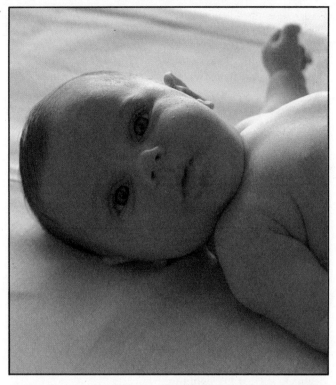

During the second month your baby will become increasingly more adapted to his surroundings. By eight or nine weeks, you will realize that major changes have occurred since his birth.

Feeding and nap routines become fairly well established, but you can still count on a few off-days, so keep your schedule flexible. Baby will spend more and more of his time awake and alert. Style differences will begin to emerge: one baby may feed leisurely while another attacks breast or bottle at a fast and furious pace. One may be content to spend much of his waking time lying in his crib; another wants to be out where the action is. But probably most important to the new parents is that almost all babies are now able to express pleasure where they could previously express only discomfort.

Although we prefer to avoid averages, by the end of this month a typical baby will weigh about 11½ pounds and measure about 23½ inches in length.

As your baby's nervous system continues to develop, all of his movements will gradually become less jerky. He still is not very coordinated, and much of the kicking and flailing of arms may seem purposeless. But it is not: this is the way baby exercises his muscles, preparing himself for the many accomplishments yet to come.

Baby's head is still wobbly, but the muscles are coming under control. Near the end of the second month, your baby will probably be able to lift his head up well while he is lying on his stomach—not an easy feat since it is still the biggest part of him and very heavy. An active baby will probably make crawling motions while on his stomach, and a few babies will even be able to move a fair distance in the crib.

Many, but not all, babies are beginning to delight in bathtime. This is probably a good time to invest in a plastic apron or simply plan a change of clothing after baby's bath. Baby's delighted kicking, pushing, splashing and slapping at the bath water will probably leave you with mixed emotions—and this is only the beginning!

With the onset of new motor activity, this is undoubtedly a good time to mention the danger of your baby's falling. A fall will happen, of course, when you least expect it, so don't underestimate your baby's abilities. A sudden reflex action coupled with a determination to be elsewhere, can flip him off his changing table the instant your back is turned. Or if his infant seat is placed on a table or other furniture that is too close to something he can grab, he can use it to pull himself overboard. Don't be misled into thinking he is incapable of performing such maneuvers just yet.

And if your baby does fall, don't feel guilty. It happens to almost all of them at least once. But *do* call your pediatrician immediately. Babies are well-protected against such mishaps, and chances are yours will suffer no ill effects once the initial fright is over. Still, with a head injury there is always the danger of possible complications, especially internal bleeding. Your doctor will tell you what to watch for during the next 24 hours to be sure this is not the case.

Just as you begin to fear that you're turning into a zombie, your baby will probably begin sleeping through the night. He may sleep as long as seven hours by the fifth week, although probably not unless he has reached the weight of eleven pounds and has overcome his early digestive problems. By the end of the month, he will hopefully be sleeping a bit longer than that. He still requires a 10 or 11 p.m. feeding, of course, but the elimination of that will be something to look forward to next month.

Some babies have a tendency to mix up their days and nights, taking their long sleep period during the daytime. The best solution is to wake baby after about four, or at most five, hours of sleep during the day. Gradually he will rearrange his sleeping patterns to conform to those of the rest of the household. A quiet baby may not get tired enough to sleep through a very long stretch just yet, but on the other hand, a quiet baby is usually less fussy when he's awake.

Although most of your baby's reflexes are beginning to taper off, the tonic neck reflex will continue for a while longer. In addition to preferring that her head be turned to a particular side, baby will also exhibit definite preferences in sleeping position. With some babies the preference is extremely strong; others are content to be shifted occasionally. For decades authoritative opinions seesawed between whether a baby should best sleep on his back or his abdomen. Today most professionals advocate satisfying baby's natural urge. Contrary to the old fears, a baby sleeping on his back is not in danger of choking. A baby sleeping on his stomach is in no danger of smothering unless his crib has been needlessly filled with blankets.

With increased activity, your baby may begin to spit up more than previously. As we mentioned in the last chapter, as long as she is gaining weight regularly (which she probably is) there is nothing to worry about except the nuisance. If you are breast-feeding or using prepared formula, you will at least have the satisfaction of knowing that the vomitus is not as foul-smelling as that from cow's milk.

Last month your bottle-fed baby was already able to discriminate between milk and sugar water; now he is also able to express his intense approval (or otherwise) of what he is drinking. If he is breast-feeding, he may begin to show a preference for one breast, even refusing to suck if his wishes are thwarted. Most likely this is an additional effect of the tonic neck reflex; too much sleeping on one side of the head may even result in a flattening of that side of the head.

The flattening is not serious, but neither is it attractive. If you notice your baby's head becoming misshapen, you will want to discuss it with your pediatrician. Usually turning the crib around (so baby has to look to the opposite side to check the goings on about him) and hanging bright objects on the neglected side of the crib will stimulate interest in trying another head position. Sometimes elevating the crib mattress an inch or two on the preferred side will encourage the head to shift position by gravity.

The second month discloses the first coordinating of baby's senses: audio and visual, as he begins to look toward an interesting sound; visual and sucking, as he begins to suck at the sight of the bottle.

Your baby's eyes can now more easily track a moving object,

first horizontally, then up and down, and a bit later in a circular pattern. He may express preferences for what he likes to look at. If given options, he will choose bright colors over neutral tones (even though he probably does not yet actually "see" in color). He prefers moving objects to stationary ones and three-dimensional to two-dimensional. Baby listens more actively now and to more different kinds of sounds, including those he makes himself. He has begun to vocalize as though in response to what he hears.

Sucking is still a highly satisfactory activity for baby, and she can now more reliably connect hand with mouth. The sucking instinct represents a strong need—extremely so in some babies—and there is no need to even consider interfering with it for many months yet. Much controversy has risen over the years about the respective merits of thumb and pacifier. One school of thought has it that the thumb is the "natural" way, and a pacifier looks like someone stuffed a plug in baby's mouth to quiet him. Proponents of the pacifier insist that the device has the advantage of being totally removable after a certain age, and that it does not push against the developing upper front teeth as a thumb does.

The arguments are reasonably valid both ways, although most dentists are now in general agreement that thumb-sucking, even continued into the second and third year, probably has far less influence on the position of a child's teeth than was once supposed. If you feel strongly opposed to pacifiers, do not use one. You will only convey to your baby that you are in some way opposed to his sucking. If you do opt for the pacifier, don't use it *all* the time. Baby needs to experiment with his

thumb and fingers too. The pacifier is intended to supplement baby's sucking needs, not merely to quiet him whenever he cries. (Used in that manner, it becomes more a crutch for mother than for her baby.)

Mouthing has begun in earnest, not only of baby's own hands but also of whatever he manages to clutch in his hand and raise to his mouth. This mouthing activity is part of the way in which he learns what is part of his own body and what is separate. With hand in mouth, for instance, he experiences the double sensation to both his mouth and his hand; with a nipple there is, of course, only sensation to his mouth.

Obviously, baby's new abilities create an interest in additional sensory stimulation. Homemade crib devices may be made from heavy elastic to which are attached any variety of objects: colored spoons, rattles, large wooden beads, spools, wooden clothespins (well-sanded), bright bangle bracelets, miniature stuffed animals—whatever you think might be appealing. Do be sure there are no removable small parts that baby might choke on. Safe crib toys are a delight to baby. He learns that his environment will respond to him: if he bats at his toys, they will dance or make funny noises.

A mirror on the side of his changing table is another source of pleasure. It is also an excellent learning tool, although it will be some months yet before your baby realizes that the other baby he's looking at is himself.

Sensory stimulation is important, but no amount of it will substitute for human interaction. Even a well-equipped crib is not the place for baby to spend all his waking hours. He needs to learn about the rest of his home and, being a social animal, sometimes he just wants company. Take advantage of the infant seat to move him around with you or, if you feel up to it, a back carrier may be even better.

Father represents still a different kind of stimulation. He should be encouraged to give baby an occasional bottle and be taught how to change and otherwise care for his new baby. Playing together will be richly rewarding for both and will hopefully establish the beginning of a good father/child relationship. Sometimes a mother needs to urge her husband's involvement. He may feel inept at handling such a young baby, or he may have been brought up with the outmoded notion that fathers simply do not become involved with their babies. Not so. Don't let either your husband or your baby miss out on this very important aspect of their lives.

Your baby is now more aware of you as something other than a dispenser of meals. He is becoming more responsive with his feedback. When you speak face to face with him, there may perhaps be a ten-second lag, but then he may react with a smile or work his mouth as though to answer you when you speak.

Baby is also very sensitive to the pleasurable sounds of the human voice. We mentioned in the last chapter that baby will stop sucking to listen to a new sound. By now he promptly returns to the business at hand and pays no further attention, *unless* the sound is that of the human voice. Then he will interrupt his sucking several more times as though waiting to discover what the voice is going to do next.

Your baby continues to gaze intently at faces, studying each feature now as though committing the entire picture to memory. Perhaps these mental images are what help him in later months to wait less impatiently when he calls for attention. He is beginning to be able to change focus and can probably adjust from six to twelve inches in distance from his eyes.

Baby may become somewhat fussy when a sitter comes to stay with him. There is no fear involved yet; the difficulty lies primarily in the fact that a comparative stranger is unlikely to offer the same set of cues and responses that his mother (or father) does. As he becomes better able to absorb the characteristics of others, the fussiness will subside.

Near the beginning of the second month, a red rash commonly appears on baby's face and neck that will last for about four to six weeks. It is presumed to be partly associated with the final disappearance of the mother's hormones. But the major factor is probably that this is the age at which baby's oil and sweat glands begin to function. There is no need to treat the rash; most products will simply irritate it further. As the glands become more mature, the rash will go away by itself.

The problem of diaper rash is another matter, however, and it can sometimes become severe. Keeping the diaper area carefully cleaned and protected by a thin layer of zinc ointment will help prevent it, but occasional attacks seem to be inevitable. There is a greater tendency for diaper rash to appear once solid foods have become a regular part of baby's diet. A light case can continue to be treated with zinc ointment and by trying to avoid keeping baby in wet or soiled diapers for prolonged periods of time. If the rash doesn't clear up in a day or two, or if it becomes noticeably worse, you should call your doctor.

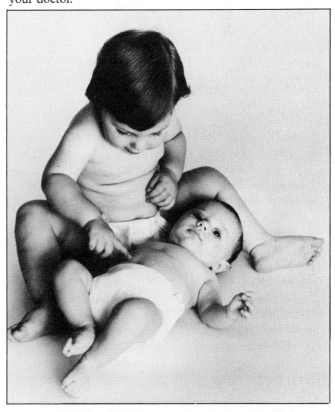

On the other hand, under normal conditions it is not necessary to rush baby into a dry diaper each time he becomes a bit wet. A few mothers seem to develop an aversion to the thought of a wet diaper and assume baby feels the same way. He doesn't, although a few may become uncomfortable from a b.m. that stays around too long. By all means, avoid communicating to your baby any unusually negative feelings you may have toward soiled diapers.

Problems with a stuffy nose may persist, now irritated by remains of spit-up milk near the back of the nasal passages. Dry air and lint from blankets (especially new ones) may contribute. Baby will not usually breathe through his mouth and instead continues his rattley nasal breathing, which undoubtedly creates more distress to listening adults than it does to baby. Using a humidifier and raising baby's head a few inches will both probably bring some relief.

Similarly, lint and accumulated mucus in baby's nose may cause him to sneeze frequently. Since he is unable to blow his nose, this is the only way he has of attempting to clear his nasal passages. Sneezing is not likely to indicate a cold at this age since baby is still protected from such infections by the presence of your antibodies, which he was born with.

Hiccups are usually very disturbing to mothers but not to babies. They are merely the result of a still immature digestive system and do not indicate that there is anything wrong with the way baby is being fed. The occurrence of hiccups is almost universal among young babies, and since there is really nothing you can do about them anyway, you can safely ignore them. Baby would cry if he were really uncomfortable.

The condition known as cradle cap may appear at about the age of six weeks. It is usually most severe over the "soft spot" area, probably due in part to the mother's reluctance to wash that area vigorously. (Washing won't hurt; the spot is protected with a tough, almost canvas-like covering.) The occurrence of cradle cap has really nothing else to do with cleanliness, however; it is simply a condition that happens to some babies. It does not hurt or itch. Your doctor will recommend a preparation that usually eliminates it with a minimum of fuss.

There are a few other areas that need not cause concern but often do. Forceps bruises may remain as tiny lumps of scar tissue beneath the skin. They will disappear in time. Your baby's legs may still be bowed as a result of their position in the uterus. Almost without exception, if your baby is receiving adequate nutrition, his legs will straighten as he begins standing on them. Some parents complain that their baby's eyes aren't the same size, which is another example of unequal development of muscle tone. The smaller eye will "catch up" eventually. Dry skin is sometimes a problem, particularly in the winter when it is aggravated by indoor heating. Fewer baths will help. But do clean the diaper area thoroughly every day. And, in or out of the tub, don't neglect the creases of the navel. That area, too, requires a daily cleaning.

The final concern you may be having is about you. If you're like most new mothers, some days you feel as though you haven't really accomplished anything except to get tired. And you probably can't help wondering once in a while if all your efforts are really worthwhile since your baby rarely shows much response anyway.

The answer to that is an unequivocal yes. Compared to a few months from now, your baby may not be displaying much physical response. But all of his waking hours are spent in watching, listening, absorbing and learning. When you cuddle and feed him, he experiences the kind of deep satisfaction that will profoundly influence his future. He cannot tell or show you yet, but you are a very special lady in his life, and he loves you dearly.

development chart

PHYSICAL	SENSORYMOTOR	INTELLECTUAL	SOCIAL
Reflex control beginning to disappear as actions become more voluntary. Cycles arms and legs quite smoothly. Can hold head up at 45° angle for a few seconds. When held vertically at torso, tries to hold head up. When sitting, head remains fairly erect but is still wobbly. Grasp more voluntary. Holds object for a few moments or longer. May bat at objects. Sleeps 7 hours at night.	Stares indefinitely at surroundings. Coordinates eye movements in a circle when watching a light or object. Visually tracks from outer corner of eye past midline of body. Moving or contoured objects hold attention longer. Fixates on one of two objects shown. Startles at sudden sounds or shows facial response. Definite listening to sound. Vocalizing probably in response to inner stimuli. Body tone improves.	Becomes excited in anticipation of objects. Begins to anticipate their movements. Reacts with generalized body movements and attempts to grab an attractive object. May begin showing preference for right or left side. Studies own hand movements. Clearly discriminates among voices, people, tastes, proximity and object sizes. Coordinating senses: looking for sound; sucking at sight of bottle.	Able to exhibit distress, excitement or delight. Can quiet self with sucking. Visually prefers person to object. Watches person alertly and directly and follows moving person with eyes. Responds to person's presence with excitement, arm- and leg-waving, panting and/or vocalizing. Quiets in response to holding or to person's voice or face. Stays awake longer if people interact with him. Enjoys bath.

Note: These charts are to be regarded as guidelines only. Many babies will perform each activity earlier or later than indicated.

crawling

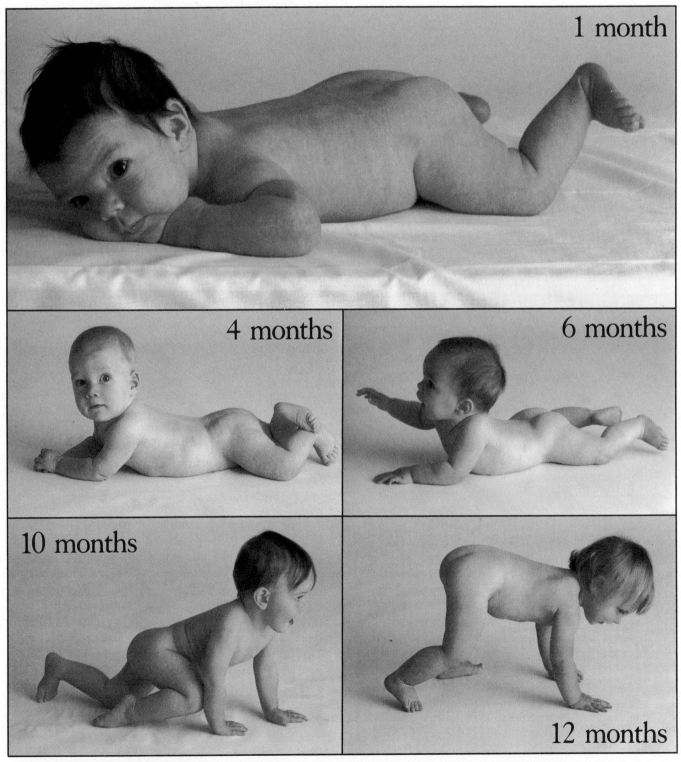

1 month

4 months

6 months

10 months

12 months

He answers with assorted noises when he's spoken to and expects those around him to do the same.

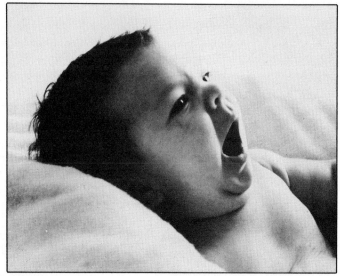

The third month heralds the onset of a whole new world for your baby—and for you. One day you will walk into his room to be greeted by a smile that seems to come from his entire body as he wiggles and kicks and reaches toward you. You can now expect your baby to be smiling pretty regularly.

Your baby has begun to indicate distinct needs and preferences. The combination of his environment and the traits and temperament of heredity are producing a definite personality. He is less inner-directed now. No longer is he governed solely by his immediate physical needs; he's learning to enjoy other aspects of the human presence. He is particularly interested in the human face, especially that part between the tip of the nose and the hairline.

Your baby's head is much less wobbly now, and with help he can maintain a semi-sitting position. When lying on his stomach, he can now lift his chest a short distance. The tonic neck reflex has almost disappeared, and by the end of the month he may voluntarily turn his head to look around him. When you stand him up, his legs stay bent, but his head will remain upright for a short time, and he may try to push with his feet.

Baby can now raise his arms from the sides of his body and bring both hands together at the center of his body. He is coordinating the looking/grasping/sucking complex, or in other words, he tries to put everything he sees into his mouth. Many mothers become needlessly alarmed at all the "dirty" objects that baby manages to get his mouth around. Don't allow him to handle anything with small parts that might choke him or anything that is obviously unclean (such as a used spoon), but other than that there's no need to worry too much. No one lives in a sterile world. Baby, too, must become accustomed to the microorganisms about him.

At last, by the end of the month your baby should be sleeping about ten hours at night. The time he wakes in the morning *may* be determined by the hour at which he has his evening bottle, but not necessarily. Some babies seem to have a built-in alarm clock that wakes them at 6 a.m. (or earlier) regardless of what time they're put to bed.

If you have been using a bassinette, now is the time to switch your baby to a full-sized crib. He needs the extra room, and if he's very active, a bassinette can soon become a dangerous place for him to be. If he's been sleeping in your room, it's also time to move him elsewhere.

Sleeping patterns differ. Many babies show an even more pronounced preference of position than they did earlier and may refuse to go to sleep any other way. It's not uncommon for a baby to cry himself to sleep. The crying seems to rid him of tensions that otherwise prevent his transition from waking to sleeping. Babies who sleep on their stomachs often exhibit a "nesting" routine in which they almost appear to burrow into the mattress.

Sometimes a baby will continue to waken for short periods during the night. He may fuss, perhaps crying a little or just making noises and sucking his fingers. These semi-alert periods occur as natural segments of the sleep cycle. Adults, too, go through similar repeated patterns during sleep but have generally become conditioned to not actually awaken during the light sleep phases. Your baby will also gradually learn to stop waking as long as a parent doesn't encourage him by rushing in to make sure he's all right. Doing that will only convince him that he can't get back to sleep unless mother or father is there to comfort him. Without you he will devise his own ways of settling back into slumber again.

If your baby has difficulty in getting to sleep when you first put him to bed at night, it may be that he has not been wide enough awake during his nonsleeping hours. Don't leave him in his crib too long when he's awake; he needs to make the association now between his crib and sleeping. On the other hand, he may not sleep well if he has had too much stimulation, particularly just before bedtime, or if he has been awake for too long a time. Use the same routine each time you put him to bed, whether at night or naptime. A consistent routine will help condition him to relax.

Your baby is now learning to wait a short time for his feedings. He may be content to play in the crib for a little while and may very well continue some of the play into feeding time. If he is being fed some solid foods already, he will happily bat at the spoon and his dish, seemingly much more interested in touching his dinner than eating it. At bottle or breast time, too, he will probably carry on bits of play, letting go of the nipple to smile or to make a few noises. You may find some of these play moments annoying if you're in a hurry, but as Dr. T. Berry Brazelton puts it in *Infants and Mothers,* to a baby they are "solid gold." Baby's physiological needs are being met, and he is at this time his happiest and most contented self.

By the beginning of the third month, your baby has probably become less fussy, and by the end of the month colic problems will have begun to wane. Of course, this doesn't mean she'll hardly cry at all anymore. A cycle of crying at the end of the day may persist for a while yet. Your baby may even scream until she seems to stop breathing and turn blue. But this performance only affects your nervous system, not hers.

By now you will have begun to recognize your baby's crying language: when he's hungry, in pain, just signaling for attention, or bursting forth with the irregular and irritating yells of colic. Sometimes your baby just cries because he's tired and has trouble "letting go" of his exciting world so that he can go to sleep. At other times he cries from boredom and is asking for some kind of stimulation rather than soothing. For the most part, the decreased crying and general fussiness of the three-month-old is brought about by the fact that he now has better things to do—even if that amounts mostly to looking around, waving his arms and moving his hands.

With the waning of the tonic neck reflex, your baby now has better voluntary control over how he chooses to turn his head. He can turn toward a sound with more certainty and is more easily able to follow a moving person with his eyes.

Color is now becoming an important part of your baby's vision. For some time to come, he will continue to prefer the brighter shades. Although he can differentiate between vivid hues, pastel colors still tend to run together into muddiness. Many manufacturers of baby toys have begun to realize this, which is why today you'll see so many more playthings in bright reds, blues or greens, for example, rather than the older versions in light pink and pale blue. Even baby's clothes are now made in a variety of brighter shades, and many have interesting designs for him to examine.

Your baby is now vocalizing much more. Voices or music not only quiet him when he's fussy but also prompt him to try to reply. He burbles and coos in response to a voice. When you hear him humming at other times, you can be sure he's signaling a good mood. He is also learning a trick: he can blow bubbles with saliva.

Baby's interest in faces continues, and he is very responsive to all of them; mother and toy clown alike will elicit a grand smile. He appears perplexed by a face in profile, however, and seems unable to associate it with the same face that looks at him full on. This suggests that baby needs you to *look* at him while he's feeding, rather than half looking away to read a book or watch television.

Your baby's hands are becoming one of the focal points of his waking hours. He spends a great deal of time watching the movements of hands and fingers and will register surprise when they reappear after having left his field of vision. He still has difficulty keeping his hands in view sometimes, but even though his eyes lose them, his mouth can still find them (or vice versa, depending on how you look at it). He now uses his hand to bat at toys or other nearby objects of interest and is beginning to grasp voluntarily, though without much purpose. If he drops what he has been holding, he still assumes it has mysteriously vanished and doesn't try to search for it with either his hands or eyes. Everything within reach he must touch, feel, manipulate.

Up to this time your baby has held his hands in a fisted position. Sometimes during this month that will change and will gradually be replaced by hands held loosely clenched; at times they will even be totally unflexed. Now baby has an even more interesting sight to view as he studies his hands; four fingers and a thumb provide more variations than a simple fist. Individual finger movements and intense staring at them will occupy much of your baby's time during this month.

Part of the reason for this is that now, for the first time, he is capable of close analysis of detailed objects that are nearby. This increased sophistication of his visual abilities also enables him to look at these objects with greater skill and speed and to glance from point to point along the surface of such objects. By the end of this month your baby's visual powers will be almost fully mature.

Now when baby drops a toy, he will wait for it to be retrieved; no longer has it disappeared into the depths of the unknown. Almost daily you can watch his fascination as he discovers new objects. You will occasionally puzzle over why he prefers some playthings to those that *you* think are more interesting. There's no real answer to that; for the most part, only baby knows why he likes what he likes. (Unfortunately, his social finesse is not well enough developed for him to at least *pretend* he likes the lovely new toy your favorite aunt has just brought him.)

Even with baby's increased self-play, he obviously continues to need interaction with other people. He is learning to communicate in a variety of ways. While on his mother's lap with the two of them looking into each other's eyes, baby may break the gaze by looking away. Mother may then glance away, and when baby looks back and sees he has "lost" her, he will fuss for her to turn back to him: this is a nice game, and he wants it to continue.

He answers with assorted noises when he's spoken to and expects those around him to do the same. By the end of the month, he will happily maintain a conversation of oohs and ahs for as long as 20 minutes. Occasionally, the dialogue will merge into a duet as speaker and listener each take a deep breath and together come out with the same sound. There will be no question in your mind how much your baby delights in this routine.

Sensory stimulation of all varieties is becoming even more important to your baby. This is the way he learns about his world. When he's awake, for the most part he no longer wants to just cuddle. He wants you to talk to him, play with him, show him new things and make noises for him. Most definitely he will protest being left alone for very long at one time.

He will enjoy handling, or at least touching, almost any safe object you give him, usually preferring the novel over the familiar. He not only wants to see the shape and color, but also he wants to feel it. He enjoys different textures and is becoming acquainted with a variety of them: there's the hard rattle, the fuzzy dog, smooth wooden boat, squashy beanbag, velvety cloth, metal bell, glossy apple, rubber duck and bumpy sofa pillow. He learns that there are different kinds of hard and different degrees of cold. He learns that some things change shape; that some stay in the new shape when he lets go of them but others return to their original form. He will experiment for long periods of time to see if the spongy squeeze toy *always* pops back into place after he lets go. By repetition he is learning a basic principle of physics.

Tell him the parts of his body as you change and bathe him.

Long before he is able to talk, he will be able to point out his foot or his ear when requested. He may enjoy watching you play peekaboo games with him but can't play them with you yet; he doesn't really understand what you're doing. He is almost sure to enjoy "This little piggy went to market." He is fascinated when you shake your head, clap your hands or stick out your tongue at him.

An active baby demands a certain amount of attention, and simply because he is active he is likely to get it. Yet it may be the quiet baby who actually *needs* more stimulation. If yours is a baby who seems content to lie in her crib during a good part of her waking hours, and particularly if she's not especially responsive when you go to get her up, don't assume that she prefers to be alone. Conversely, whether your baby is active, quiet or in between, don't overdo the stimulation. Especially as naptime or bedtime approaches, help him gently calm down. Now is the time for rocking, cuddling and perhaps soft music. Too much stimulation can overwhelm and frighten a young baby, and he will begin to reject it. In the right amount, he will learn more from his environment and be able to remember it; he'll be better able to use the information, and eventually he can be expected to achieve greater potential.

Frankly, it is difficult to visualize a mother checking a timetable and instructing her baby that it's now play period, whether he feels like it or not. Common sense is the best rule. Sometimes your baby will waken ravenously hungry; some days you will want playtime kept to a minimum so he'll take an early afternoon nap and leave time to do errands afterwards; other times you may want him to take a later nap so you'll have extra time to prepare a special meal for dinner guests that evening. Of course, baby won't always conform to your wishes, either. At the most unlikely times he will get sleepy when you had planned to keep him up playing for a while. (All you can do is try!)

Your husband will probably enjoy more time with baby now too. There's less fear on the father's part that he will mishandle and accidentally hurt his son or daughter. Then, too, he will be more enthusiastic in general now that baby can finally "do something." Continue to encourage the relationship; it's an important one. (Besides, it gives you a much needed break.)

Now that your baby can more easily and quickly discern the difference among faces he sees, he may "complain" about being left with a sitter. But you need some time out, and as long as you have a reliable person to stay with your baby, he will suffer no harm.

The baby-sitter difficulty at this stage is only the first of several more periods with which you will have to cope in the future. As your baby's development changes, so does his attitude toward "outsiders"—but for different reasons at different stages. Right now, his reluctance has nothing to do with any real fears, so now is the best time for him to begin learning that you will return in a reasonable length of time and

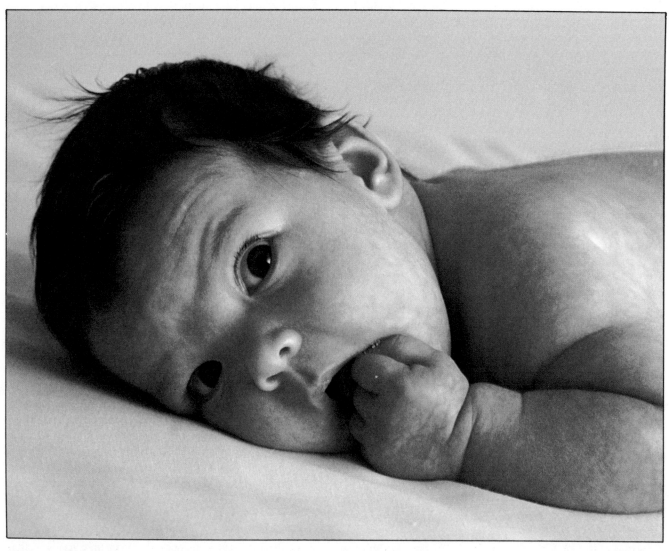

that nothing bad is going to happen to him in the meantime. Occasionally, of course, you may sense that your baby is genuinely unhappy with his sitter. It isn't logical to assume that every sitter, even first-rate ones, will have a good rapport with every baby. Try having the baby-sitter spend more time while you are there and can explain more fully the details of baby's routine and what he particularly likes and dislikes. As a last resort, you can always hire a different sitter. It's easiest for baby, of course, if you try to arrange for the same one or two sitters as much as possible rather than continually switching to new ones. But there will be times when you may need to hire a comparative stranger, and in spite of baby's protests, he will suffer no damage.

A mother of more than one child often begins to worry now that she is devoting too little attention to the older one (or ones). Possibly she is, since there are only a certain number of hours in the day. What is most important is that you help your older child retain her own sense of identity and importance to the family. Stress her "grown-up" abilities and the privileges she has earned by being older. At all costs, avoid ending every other sentence with "because of the baby." ("We can't go to the park today...", "You can't have your friend come to visit...", "I can't play that game with you right now...") Even an adult would grow to dislike a person who hampered his daily activities that often.

Now, before your baby becomes too active, is the best time to begin babyproofing your house or apartment. As with almost every other aspect of baby care, two schools of thought have reigned: one is that nothing should be moved so baby can learn right away what may and may not be touched; the other is that everything reachable should be moved so that baby never has to hear "No!" shouted at him.

It seems almost obvious that a middle ground is best. There's no need for the family to exist in barren living quarters for the next year or so. It won't be very interesting for baby either. On the other hand, you will want to temporarily move out of reach some of your more valuable books and trinkets. Put the less important books on the bottom shelves, and use the less breakable, or at least replaceable, items on your coffee and end tables. Your baby will need to understand "no" sooner or later; while he's learning, it might as well be among articles that are comparatively expendable.

As you go about this business of baby-tending, you will gradually learn how to better communicate with him. You'll become more sensitive to his needs, which may not always be the same as his wishes. There will be times when he has been overstimulated and must be calmed, and there will be times when he needs to be perked up with a new plaything or change of scene.

Get down on the floor with him for a "baby's-eye-view" of his world. You'll be surprised how different it looks to exist in a maze of table and chair legs. It may have been a long time since you really looked at sunbeams dancing on the wall or studied the patterns in your living room rug. Seeing things through baby's eyes can contribute immensely to a mutually satisfying relationship.

development chart

PHYSICAL	SENSORYMOTOR	INTELLECTUAL	SOCIAL
Moves arms and legs vigorously. May move arms together, then legs together, or arm and leg on one side of body, then the other. When picked up, brings body up compactly. Lies on stomach with legs flexed. When on stomach, holds chest up and head erect for about 10 seconds. May lift head for many minutes. Leans on elbows while on stomach. Able to sit with support. Head wobbling is minimal. Begins to bat at objects. Reaches with both arms, starting at sides and bringing together in front of body. Object may be contacted with closed fists.	Follows a slowly moving object with eyes and head from one side of body to the other. Can view fingers individually instead of in fisted position. Stops sucking to listen. Looks and sucks at same time. Visually seeks source of sound by turning head and neck. Distinguishes speech sounds from other sounds. Grasp reflex disappearing and hands usually held open. May voluntarily hold and wave a toy.	Begins to show memory. Waits for expected reward like feeding. Begins to recognize and differentiate family members or other persons close to him. Explores own face, eyes and mouth with hand. Responds to most kinds of stimulation with entire body.	Smiles easily and spontaneously. Crying decreases dramatically. Facial expression, body tone and vocalizing increase. Gurgles and coos in response to sounds. Social stimulation more important. Responds with total body to face he recognizes. Protests when left alone. Cries differently when mother leaves him than when others do. Reacts differently to mother's presence. Tries to attract her attention when she is nearby. Patterns of eating, sleeping and alertness clearly regulated.

Note: These charts are to be regarded as guidelines only. Many babies will perform each activity earlier or later than indicated.

Your baby is approaching the age of showing off, and if she is outgoing enough, she'll need little encouragement to keep it up for hours.

As your baby enters his fourth month, he no longer qualifies as a newborn. Reflex responses continue to diminish as voluntary actions assume control. Rarely does the startle reflex shatter your baby's composure. The rooting reflex is virtually nonexistent since baby knows and can easily see exactly what he's looking for. Many of his movements have slowed down now that he has better control over the parts of his body, and all of his actions have become less machine-like except when he's tired.

This month is probably an ideal time for photography now that your baby is beginning to look more like some of the pictures you see in magazines. His hair has most likely begun to change, both in color and texture. You may not have noticed, but during the past few weeks he has been losing the hair he had at birth, and it is being replaced by his new permanent hair. This process will continue for another month or two.

Your baby's eye color, too, may have changed. The blue eyes that most Caucasians are born with will probably already have begun to muddy in brunette babies, eventually turning brown or an in-between color. If your baby's eyes are still blue by the age of six months, you can be pretty sure they will remain that color. Black babies are generally born with more or less colorless eyes, which gradually turn brown.

The presence of pigmentation spots known as "Mongolian spots" near the base of the spine almost invariably indicates that a baby will be brunette, no matter what color hair and eyes he may have at birth. These spots will spread out and disappear in time. Your baby's skin tone is the best indicator of his future coloring.

Even more pronounced than the alterations in your baby's appearance are the changes in his physical prowess as he follows the typical head-to-toe pattern of development. His body is beginning to fill out as his muscles grow and strengthen. By the end of the month baby's head will be completely under control. He will be able to hold it steady, and when lying on his stomach will lift and hold it at a 90-degree angle. He will turn it in all directions (except backward, of course) and move it in all positions. He will be able to lift his head when lying on his back, and by pressing his chin onto his chest, be able to look at his feet.

The muscles of your baby's trunk will become much stronger during this month and the following two. His grasping strength has increased and is more flexible. While lying on his stomach, he can support the weight of his head and chest on one arm.

If your baby did not begin to roll from his back to his stomach last month, he will most likely do it now. Shortly afterward, he will roll from his stomach to his side, but most babies won't make it all the way over (stomach to back) for a few more weeks yet.

Your baby can be propped up into a sitting position now—and how he loves it! His back still needs some support, but his head remains easily erect with no prop. While on his back and holding your fingers, baby can now lift his head and legs and *almost* pull himself to a sitting position without your help. By the end of the month, his own muscles will hold him upright on your lap with only a minimum of help from you. There is less molding when he's lap-sitting, and he has begun to sense you are not actually part of his physical person. Up to now as he cuddled on your lap, he often fitted his entire body into the curves and crevices of your own, creating a oneness.

Your baby of four months delights in kicking. He holds his legs up, flexes them and bicycles in the air. Gradually he is able to lift them enough to touch his knees with his hands. Slowly, slowly in the months to come those legs will become strong enough to support his entire weight.

In the meantime, some babies will be making "swimming" motions, the first rudiments of creeping and crawling. Until he is finally able to "take off" and maneuver across the room, he may spend many of his waking hours panting, grunting, groaning and yelling. You may need to remind yourself many times that determination is considered a positive quality in adults—why not in babies?

You may notice a great deal of crackling of your baby's knees and elbows. It will disappear as her muscles grow stronger and is nothing to worry about.

Sometime during the fourth month, perhaps earlier, your pediatrician may advise you to begin introducing solid food to your baby, most likely cereal. Many babies are enthusiastic about this new taste sensation, but just as many others let you know in no uncertain terms that they will do nicely without it, thanks. Don't feel chagrined if your baby refuses solids in the beginning; the basic idea is to accustom him to other than liquid nourishment. Don't fight with your baby about food of any kind. Continue offering him just a taste or two at the specified meals. If his refusal is adamant, your doctor may suggest that you wait and try again in another week or two. Eventually baby will get the hang of it and learn to enjoy at least some of your offerings.

It is important that you follow your pediatrician's instructions about the introduction of solids. Only one new item should be introduced at a time, and it should be done *slowly*. The reasons are twofold: to give baby an opportunity to become familiar with each new taste and to minimize the possibility of allergic reactions.

Once solid foods become a regular part of your baby's meals, he will gradually drink less milk and may be on a three-meals-a-day schedule plus a bedtime bottle. If the time span is too long between meals, you may have to wait half an hour to an hour between solids and milk. Unless your baby is strongly opinionated about his feeding patterns, it's usually best to encourage him to eat his solids before breast or bottle. Milk is very filling to the stomach, and when it is taken first, baby may not be hungry enough to eat adequate portions of the solid foods that are fast becoming an important part of his diet. Many babies, however, appear thoroughly insulted at the idea of being offered solids before milk, particularly when they first wake up in the morning. If your baby reacts that way, you might try giving him just part of his bottle and letting him finish after he has eaten the rest of his meal.

Your baby may try to grab the spoon while you are feeding him. He's not really trying to feed himself yet; he just wants to "check it out." It's easy enough to give him a spoon of his own. Inexpensive demitasse spoons are of excellent size and shape for both you and your baby to use.

By all means, keep mealtime pleasant. This is not the time to scold or otherwise show anger, or to punish, rush or force-feed. If such actions are habitual, they may trigger the beginning of lifelong poor eating habits and most certainly will result in your baby's dissatisfaction with life in general. You need to maintain the same positive associations with mealtime that you have been providing him since birth.

When solid foods become an established part of your baby's diet, you will probably notice that his bowel movements will be fewer and more regular. And if you are breast-feeding, you are apt to encounter a few stabs of jealousy either from your husband or from other women. For some reason, many people (who *aren't* nursing) seem to think that because your baby is not so helpless as he was in his early weeks, he therefore doesn't need you all that much. Some nursing mothers do switch to a bottle about this age if they feel it's more convenient, but at least as many others continue nursing for several more months until baby is ready to drink from a cup or glass. Obviously, it's much too early to consider weaning your baby. Even if you were able to pour enough milk down him from a glass, he would be deprived of the necessary sucking satisfaction.

Drooling usually begins about this time. Although it is often assumed to be caused by teething, the association is not really clear. Your baby *may* cut his first tooth this early, but generally the first tooth does not appear before the sixth month and may be much later than that.

Drooling is sometimes profuse enough in babies that their faces and necks are constantly wet, and the result of that is often a rash. If your baby begins to develop a skin irritation, you can protect his face with petroleum jelly and pat a little baby powder or cornstarch on the creases of his neck. (If the rash should become severe you will, of course, want to consult your pediatrician.)

If your baby is actually beginning to teethe at this age, you'll probably notice him pulling at his jaw or his ear. The same set of muscles controls both areas, so it may be difficult at first for you to decide whether your baby is suffering from an earache or teething pain. Rubbing his gums will give you a fast answer: if he's teething, he'll respond with a loud noise.

Some babies seem to be bothered very little from teething; others are in one stage or another of discomfort throughout the entire process. Should your baby begin to show signs of pain, keep a supply of different types of teething rings in the refrigerator. The coldness makes his gums feel better.

Your baby now ought to be sleeping between ten and eleven hours at night with two or three naps during the day. To help your baby best achieve quiet, refreshing sleep, ideally he should be put to bed at the first signs of fatigue. As every mother knows, this is not always possible. Do make an effort in that direction, however. If baby's wakeful period is extended too long, he may have difficulty falling asleep. He will also tend to waken early and be irritable during his next period of wakefulness. Particularly when your baby has been overstimulated while awake, this can sometimes set off a cycle that will remain unbroken for days.

How do you tell when your baby is tired? There are quite a number of ways, and your baby will undoubtedly develop his own particular set of signals. Obvious, of course, are yawning, rubbing the eyes and not wanting to play. But there are many babies who become *more* active as they grow tired. You will notice, however, a gradual regression to earlier kinds of activity rather than the newer things he has learned to do. His behavior will become more rhythmical, such as rolling his head, and some of the old reflexes may begin to reappear. There will be some thumb-sucking, a display of ill temper and general restlessness. More than likely, you won't need to be much of a detective to decipher your baby's sleepiness code.

By the end of the month, your baby is definitely seeing his surroundings in color. He now focuses very well and at different distances, although he still prefers to look at whatever is up to a yard in front of him rather than across the room. By the time he reaches his four-month birthday, he will be able to focus on near or distant targets as well as an adult can. His eye movements are less jerky, and he can follow a moving object or person about the room with ease. He is able to sort out and consolidate what he's looking at, and as noted Swiss psychologist Jean Piaget put it, he no longer sees his world "as though through the windows of a moving train."

Your baby's hand/eye coordination is coming under increasing control. When she was first grasping, she moved her slightly clenched hand toward a desired object until she touched it; later her hand approached the object opened wide. Now she moves with her fingers spread to the approximate size of the object. Her desire to grasp has become stronger; she manipulates better and more deliberately. This is the age when she'll begin to grab your sunglasses or pull her father's beard.

Baby can now hear almost as well as an adult. He can discern the source of weak as well as intensive sounds. If he has not already shown a response to music, he probably will begin this month.

Your baby may seem to respond to his name, but in reality he is still responding only to the sound of being spoken to. (Countless mothers are sure to disagree.) Use his name frequently when talking to him, and before many more weeks he will be answering to his name.

There is a great new interest in making sounds, and some of them will be recited over and over again as if to make sure they won't be forgotten. Many of them will be syllables that months from now will be put together into real words. Gurgles are turning to chuckles, bubbles, giggles and shrieks. He is likely to laugh loudly when tickled. This "tickle response" has not been present before. It perhaps indicates a new social awareness, but no apparent research has ever been conducted as to why a younger baby is simply not ticklish.

Now that your baby's grasping abilities have become stronger and more determined, it's time to put away the fragile mobiles and similar items. There are any number of other things to capture his interest now. His crib gym will take on a new fascination as he begins to grab a ring in each hand.

Whatever kind of playthings you purchase for your baby or receive as gifts, be sure to check them carefully for safety. Beware of brittle rattles, metal squeakers that could come loose from squeeze toys or glass eyes that might be easily dislodged from stuffed animals. Unless such eyes are firmly locked in, it may be better to remove them yourself and embroider the animal a new pair. Avoid suspending either toys or pacifier from long strings in the crib. They can come loose and wind themselves around a baby's neck. And never, *ever* put a pacifier on a string around your baby's neck.

A few babies of this age are already developing such an attachment to a particular toy or blanket that at some future date you may not be able to separate him from it. Such an attachment indicates a strong interest for something outside of baby's own self, a concept that few babies in their fourth month are yet able to grasp. These "loveys" do no harm whatsoever and can be a great source of comfort for a baby of any age.

Lack of stimulation may cause a baby to become fussy or drowsy. You will need to continue enriching his surroundings, and don't neglect his sense of smell. Both of you will enjoy his reactions as he sniffs at flowers, vinegar, perfume, a piece of fresh fruit and whatever else you have handy.

Your baby's smile has matured still more since last month. He now openly exhibits very definite and genuine pleasure at the sight of family members and anyone else he knows and likes. He probably hasn't learned yet that people can sometimes be disagreeable. He loves "talking" with you or with almost anyone who will converse with him. When you express approval of each new achievement, he radiates joy.

If there is an older child or children at home, continue to keep her (or them) involved with your baby. With careful supervision big brother or sister can now be allowed to hold baby for a short time. Encourage the relationship, but don't push it too strongly if you meet with resistance. Studies on learning have shown that even though a first baby receives more attention from mother, a later baby tends to learn more at an earlier age because he is learning from a sibling.

Your baby is approaching the age of showing off, and if he is outgoing enough, he'll need little encouragement to keep it up

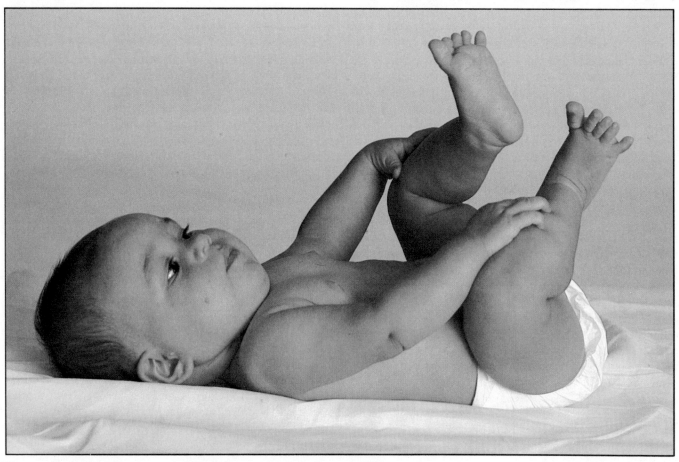

for hours. An admiring audience or new and exciting events, such as a first visit to his grandparents, may prompt this kind of prolonged behavior with near-catastrophic results. It may be days before baby's sleep patterns settle back to normal. As we have mentioned before, *over*stimulation should be avoided as much as possible.

Father continues to become ever more important to your baby's development. The voice is different, the reactions are different. In most households father spends more time playing with baby and less in the humdrum affairs of feeding, bathing and changing. Baby doutbless looks upon him as a special kind of toy.

Fathers who are home a lot and share in the baby-tending duties may not elicit exactly this same kind of specialness. Yet under those circumstances he will be recognized and responded to at about the same time as the mother is. In other words, the relationship becomes a different kind of "special." Parenthetically, numerous studies have shown that except in the case of breast-feeders, a baby shows no innate biological preference for one parent over the other. If yours happens to be a role-reversal household—with wife going off to work while husband stays home—you can rest assured that a father can be just as good a mother as mother.

Your baby is not too clear about his relationships with things. He observes, for example, that he can make his crib toys bounce by kicking. If the window curtain flutters at the same time, he does *not* know that his kicking didn't also cause the fluttering. He may lie there kicking furiously for a time as he tries to make the curtain flutter again, but it will not. Soon he lets out a few frustrated grunts that may quickly lead to full-blown howls. Such is the developing mind of the young baby. It is any wonder that a mother is often seen holding her head in exasperation as she tries to figure out what her baby is fussing about *now*?

Many mothers' emotions toward their babies begin to change about this time. As baby becomes less helpless, mother becomes less patient. Her baby begins to sense the kind of behavior that she finds unacceptable; thus are born the origins of discipline. Don't expect to accomplish much in that direction for a while yet, however. Repetition is still the key word. There is the added difficulty that much of what you might wish your baby to learn makes no sense at all to him. You may want to teach him not to push his toys out of the crib. To baby such actions merely result in a game, and it will be many months before he understands your viewpoint.

In the meantime, you'll have to muster up all the patience you can find. It helps, too, to keep your sense of humor in peak working order. Play with your baby regularly and show him affection. You and the other persons close to baby form an integral part of his development. As much as he enjoys his toys and other playthings, they always respond in the same way. But *people* can do all sorts of things!

development chart

PHYSICAL	SENSORYMOTOR	INTELLECTUAL	SOCIAL
Lies on stomach with legs extended. When on stomach, rolls from side to side. May roll from stomach or side to back. May make swimming motions and move in crib. Turns head in all directions when seated or lying down. Holds head steady and erect for short time. When on stomach lifts head at 90-degree angle. On back may crane neck forward to watch hands grasp feet. Uses hands with more agility and variety. Predictable interval between feeding and bowel movements. Sleeps about 10-11 hours at night.	Head and eyes turn in co-ordination; follows source of sound and dangling or moving object easily. Can now focus at different distances. Batting at objects becomes more accurate. May take small objects between index and second fingers. Pulls dangling object toward him and carries to mouth. Stares at place from which an object drops. Distinguishes and displays an interest in different smells. Interested in making new sounds and imitates several tones. Quieted by music. Splashes and kicks in bath; lifts head well while in tub.	Responsive periods may be an hour or more at a time. Has memory span of 5-7 seconds. Smiles and vocalizes more to an actual face than to an image. Discriminates among faces; knows mother and other family members; probably resents strangers. Aware of strange situation. Begins to adjust responses to people. Becomes aware of distinctness of his own act from the external result.	Vocalizes to initiate socializing, either by making sounds or by coughing or clicking tongue. Smiles more openly. Laughs while socializing; cries if play is disrupted. Vocalizes moods, enjoyment, indecision and protest. Interested in and may smile at mirror image. Responds to and enjoys handling. Enjoys play, games and other forms of socializing. Shows interest in playthings; may indicate preference for one or two toys. May interrupt feedings with play. Attempts to soothe self. Eating/sleeping routines become better established.

Note: These charts are to be regarded as guidelines only. Many babies will perform each activity earlier or later than indicated.

Baby may be able to get one leg up under his tummy by the end of the month, signaling that he's just about ready to begin creeping.

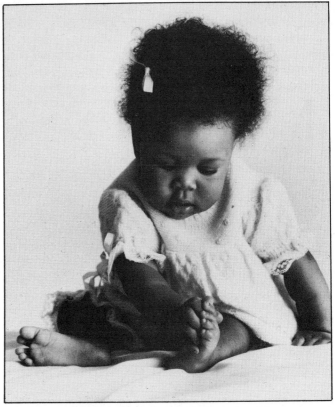

By the end of the fifth month, your baby will have just about doubled his birthweight. From now until the end of the first year, his rate of weight gain will be approximately half of what it has been during the earliest months—or in other words, about a pound a month. Weight gain might be somewhat irregular though; some babies tend to gain in spurts.

Your baby's life is busy now. He eagerly looks forward to each new day and spends a great deal of time practicing his motor skills, talking, listening and exploring everything within reach. This is a time of transition—between attachment to the familiar and a desire to explore.

Almost every day you will notice subtle, or sometimes not-so-subtle, changes in your baby's motor activities. As he sits on your lap, he will sometimes inch away from you, looking down at the floor as though trying to figure out the best way to get there. An attentive mother will understand his wants and help him down.

Sometime during this month when your baby is lying on his stomach, you may see him doing an "airplane," a movement in which both arms and both legs are stretched out, with head lifted and back bent. This is an excellent exercise for strengthening the back and neck muscles (for adults as well as babies). Baby may be able to get one leg up under his tummy by the end of the month, and a very active baby can slowly propel himself across the crib on his stomach just by kicking his legs.

Your baby is probably rolling over, back to stomach, quite easily now; a few babies can also turn stomach to back. The likely result is that your days, and possibly your nights, will be interrupted by the persistent screams of baby wanting to be turned onto his back again. The best you can do is to keep on showing him how to turn himself and hope that it won't be too much longer before his muscles are strong enough so that he can do it. Usually two or three weeks of that behavior is about all you'll have to put up with.

This is also a period during which your baby tends to come very quickly to full wakefulness in the morning, almost as if he can't wait to get started with the day's business. More often than not he wakens long before the rest of the household is ready to rise. Try putting a favorite toy or two in his crib after he goes to sleep at night. He may then be content to play by himself for at least a little while after he wakes up.

Some days your baby may only take one nap. It's best for both of you, however, if you encourage him to take a second rest period in his crib, even if he doesn't actually fall asleep. (You both need that extra little break in the day.)

The ingredients in solid foods tend to make baby's urine and bowel movements more irritating to his skin than breast milk or formula did. Consequently, diaper rash often becomes more of a problem at this age.

Now that your baby is more active, hot weather may cause her to develop heat rash, or miliaria (not to be confused with malaria). Keep her in as little clothing as possible, bathe her frequently and dust the affected areas with a little baby powder or cornstarch.

This is a good time to invest in a bouncer or other type of play chair. Your baby is becoming too active to safely remain unattended in his infant seat. You may continue to find the infant seat convenient for feeding him though, at least until he is sitting well enough to manage comfortably in a highchair.

Feeding your baby is now becoming a major undertaking. Meals may stretch out interminably as baby insists on playing between each bite. After you finally get a spoonful of food inside him, he is likely to open his mouth and let it ooze back down his chin. As you patiently scrape it off and spoon it back into his mouth, you can't help but wonder what tactic he's plotting next. Unfortunately, he will come up with a number of them: blowing it out is a special favorite. Dr. T. Berry Brazelton tells a story of a father who wore a raincoat whenever he fed his son.

You will sometimes be tempted to laugh at your baby's antics, and even more often you'll be tempted to scold. It's best to avoid doing either. Mealtime should be kept pleasant, but if you show any indication of approving a fistful of spinach thrown at the wall, baby is sure to put on an even better performance for you at the next meal.

You can be somewhat more persistent now in encouraging baby to eat his solids, assuming that he has already made an initial acquaintance with them. (Some pediatricians recommend waiting until this month to start solids.) Baby's need for a more balanced diet is now becoming greater than his need for an abundance of milk. Iron, nearly absent in milk, is of particular importance at this age and for many years to come. The milk requirement is now reduced to between 20 and 24 ounces a day.

Most babies enjoy most kinds of solid foods once they get used to them. They relish experimenting with the new tastes and textures, and presumably they like the feeling of satisfaction that solids leave in their stomachs. The most resistance usually comes when a new food is introduced, particularly if that food is a vegetable. You can minimize this resistance by keeping your attitude calm and reassuring. Offer the new food near the beginning of the meal, when baby is hungriest. And watch your own reactions: if you dislike a particular food, your baby may sense this and refuse to eat it. And most important, don't force baby to eat something he doesn't like. We have suggested that you make a greater effort than you did in the earlier months to encourage new foods, but that is not the same as trying to *make* baby eat.

Your pediatrician may have already offered you this tip for starting a new food: if your baby is already eating carrots, for instance, and his usual portion is four teaspoons, give him three teaspoons of carrots and one teaspoon of peas, or whatever new vegetable you are trying. The next day give him two teaspoons of each, and the day after only one teaspoon of carrots plus three teaspoons of peas. That way baby can become accustomed to the new taste gradually. This method also helps uncover any allergic reactions.

Don't start a new food if your baby has a cold or is otherwise not feeling well. His appetite will probably be decreased, and he's more likely to balk about eating much of anything. Teething sometimes affects the appetite too. If your baby refuses foods that he normally eats, you can safely ignore the problem temporarily. In addition, there will probably be a few foods and tastes that your baby simply will not like. You'll want to encourage as great a variety as possible, but there's no point in making an issue over one or two foods if he likes all the others. Wait a few weeks and try again. By then he may decide he loves it.

Your pediatrician will suggest the *approximate* portion sizes your baby should be eating. Portions will vary according to how many different kinds of foods baby is being fed at the meal. Amounts also vary from baby to baby because appetites vary. One baby may gain more weight than her next door neighbor even though she eats less and drinks less milk. That's because she is less active and burns fewer calories.

Most people today are aware that a plump baby does *not* signify a healthy baby. Overfed babies can become overweight and form more fat cells than other babies do; this is a condition that appears to linger throughout one's lifetime. A recent study in England indicates that excess weight gained during the first year of life is more significant as a predictor of later obesity than any other factor. The extra fat cells that are produced during infancy will never disappear; dieting will flatten them out, but they remain to fill up with fat again.

Obesity is currently one of America's major health problems. Don't let your baby become a victim. He will let you know when he's had enough food to eat just as he has always let you know when he's had sufficient milk to drink. Never urge him to take "just one more bite."

Soon there will need to be less time between feeding solids and milk in order to keep baby from consuming too much of the latter. Milk is a very high-calorie food, and while your baby still needs a minimum of about 20 ounces, very much more than that is likely to result in overweight.

Even though your baby is managing nicely with solid foods, it will be some time yet before he achieves a truly balanced diet. For that reason your pediatrician has probably already prescribed vitamin drops. They should be continued as a precautionary measure at least through baby's first year. Your doctor may recommend that they be taken longer.

During this period there seems to be a definite tendency toward increased sucking. Part of the reason is probably that baby is sucking for a shorter length of time from breast or bottle. But in addition, the frustrations of trying to roll over and creep seem to be contributing factors. There is a novel variation, however; some babies have now begun to suck on their toes as well as their fingers.

Reaching is the first step toward creeping. Although your baby still can't reach too far, he is intent on touching and manipulating all that's available. His eyes direct his hands now. He may transfer items from hand to hand, or he may grasp with both hands at once. Mouthing continues to be a dimension of his explorations but with a difference: he is also beginning to chew on everything (with or without teeth).

You know baby is learning to anticipate results by the way he grasps for his bottle and makes his crib toys swing. He will readily look for a dropped object but not a hidden one, even if he watches you hide it. If his hands disappear from view, he knows where they are. He may indicate distress by pulling, poking, pinching or scratching at himself. (The scientific reasons for this are still unclear except that even in adults, self-induced pain appears to override the pain one can't control, making it somewhat easier to bear.)

Your baby, boy or girl, is discovering his (or her) genitals. Even in this modern age of permissiveness, many parents are alarmed and upset by this new exploratory behavior. There is absolutely no reason to be. Baby is simply learning about his genital area in the same manner he learned about his fingers and his ears: by feeling and manipulating. The area takes on a heightened interest simply because he can't get at it any time he wants, as he can with his face or hands. The examining process will continue for many weeks or even months. Avoid conveying to your baby that you think what he is doing is "bad" or "dirty." Allow him to explore freely. Treat the situation matter-of-factly and tell your baby the correct names, penis or vagina, just as you have been doing with other parts of the body.

Vocalizing is rapidly becoming more entertaining for both baby and his audience. He can now squeal, grunt, purr, growl, spit, smack his lips, blow "raspberries" and click his tongue. A favorite trick is mock coughing, which

he can perform beautifully. He mimics many other expressions and gestures as well. His conversations have begun to assume the same inflections and intonations that are present in the voices he has been hearing. Many "sentences" end with a high note as though he were asking a question.

Your baby is now putting consonants and vowels together more and more frequently. "Da" is a favorite combination that occasionally gets doubled up into "dada," much to everyone's delight. The thrilled responses he receives help reinforce the behavior, and he will tend to repeat it more often than other combinations that come out of his mouth. Of course, he has no idea what he's saying just yet, but sooner or later he'll make the connection. In the meantime, he finds it great fun having you repeat all his new syllables back to him as he runs through his repertoire.

Listening is becoming more intense now. There are responses to more kinds of auditory stimuli, but the human voice always merits the most attention. Your baby can readily pick out your voice from among those in a roomful of people. He particularly likes to listen to rhythmic verses, including many nursery rhymes. Talk to your baby often. Tell him the names of common items he sees every day, keeping your sentences short and simple.

This month is a good time to have your baby's hearing tested. His language development, which begins soon, is directly dependent on his ability to hear well, and if there should be a moderate hearing loss, early detection could help prevent future problems.

Carriage rides become even more enjoyable for your baby now that he can be propped in a sitting position. There are so many things to see and hear and smell! He is also more easily able to amuse himself. You will need to check the toys in his crib and play yard frequently. They should be changed often, or at least rearranged. Some may need to be raised out of reach for safety's sake; others may need to be lowered now that he needs to touch as well as look at them.

Bath toys are favorites at this age. Nothing too elaborate is necessary; a few odds and ends from your kitchen, which he can use for pouring water back and forth, will make him happy. He might also enjoy a music box that he can start himself by pulling a handle or a crib gym with items that he can handle, strike or pull.

Avoid the assumption that every plaything labeled as an "educational toy" is precisely that. Unfortunately, many such toys are made to appeal to adults rather than children and babies. It will be helpful to talk to mothers with babies somewhat older than yours to learn their views on which toys have actual play value and which do not.

If your baby doesn't already have a mirror to play with, try to find him a good one now. It must be unbreakable metal, of course, about four or five inches in diameter and of good enough quality so that distortion will be minimal. Baby will enjoy looking in a full-length mirror with you now too. This is the age when he first becomes puzzled at the idea of the "mirror mother" talking in front of him while her voice is coming from behind him. Think of how hard it would be to explain the functioning of a mirror to an adult. Your baby will learn the principle of mirror images much more quickly than a grownup could and with practically no explanation.

If you haven't yet babyproofed your house or apartment, your baby's current pre-crawling stage signals that you can't wait much longer. Already she can knock over a cup of hot coffee, grab the cords of electrical appliances and initiate any number of other hazardous maneuvers that won't even occur to you until after they've already happened.

At about the age of five to six months, a bout of "stranger distress" may begin to emerge. The baby suddenly reacts with hesitation and fear to those outside the immediate family. This is probably a good time to avoid too frequent use of baby-sitters if you can. Take your baby with you now as often as possible. Before too long he won't be as easily portable as he is now.

Usually a baby becomes more sociable with outsiders if he first has the opportunity to study them from the safety of mother's (or father's) lap. Explain to strangers how best to approach your baby: generally by ignoring him and casually chatting with you. That gives baby a chance to size up the new person and make the first overtures (if he so chooses!).

It is of interest that babies as young as five months reveal greater social ease when their fathers have helped take care of them. Perhaps father contributes to baby's intellectual development in a different way. Or perhaps it is because baby has had the opportunity to become thoroughly comfortable with another person besides his mother.

During quiet periods baby will enjoy gazing into your eyes, as long as you return the gaze. It is almost as though he is trying to probe the depths of knowledge that lie behind mother's eyes. He now studies your entire body and the clothing you're wearing. Studies indicate, however, that he can't yet remember your face once it disappears from view. (But that is a difficult task even for an adult.)

As baby becomes more mobile, it will be necessary for you to impose more restraints, which in turn will result in more resistance on your baby's part. These are the initial steps toward discipline, and you might as well keep your sense of humor. You need to realize that your baby's behavior is part of his normal development. If instead you view his behavior as flaunting authority, that could mean trouble. Your baby needs a certain amount of stability and regularity. But if you see that you're creating problems by expecting more than your baby is capable of handling, you will need to be more flexible. Your baby already senses that when you feel good, he feels good too. As long as you're not too demanding now, when he is able he will try to be more cooperative—at least *some* of the time.

development chart

PHYSICAL	SENSORYMOTOR	INTELLECTUAL	SOCIAL
On stomach rocks like airplane with limbs extended and back arched; pushes on hands and draws up knees. On back lifts head and shoulders well. Brings feet to mouth and sucks on toes. Rolls from stomach to back. May locomote by rocking, rolling and twisting; on back by kicking against flat surface. When seated or pulled to sit, head is balanced steadily and held continuously erect. Wants to touch, hold, turn, shake, mouth and taste objects. Easily pulled to standing position. May hold bottle with one or both hands. May transfer objects from hand to hand.	Grasp more steady; raises hand in vicinity of object; glances between hand and object; gradually closes gap and grasps. Reaches for object with either one or both hands. Aim is good when reaching and grasping a large ring. Plays with rattle placed in hands. Imitates sounds and movements deliberately.	Alert almost two hours. Looks around in new situation; turns head deliberately toward a sound to follow vanishing object. Visually searches for fast-moving objects. Leans over to look for fallen object. Recognizes familiar objects. Remembers his own actions in the immediate past. Has mental model for the human face. Knows parents and siblings; may resent strangers, particularly women. Vocalizing takes on inflections and intonations of adult voices. Utters vowel sounds and a few consonants (d, b, l, m).	Responds to human sounds more definitively; turns head; seems to look for speaker. Smiles or vocalizes to make social contact and gain attention. Interrupts others' conversations by vocalizing. Stops crying when being talked to. Smiles at human faces and voices. Makes face in imitation. May learn to tease. Expresses protest; resists adult who tries to take toy. Discriminates self and mother in mirror.

Note: These charts are to be regarded as guidelines only. Many babies will perform each activity earlier or later than indicated.

This is a time of abrupt mood changes, wholehearted and undisguised. Baby may display her temper when something doesn't suit her.

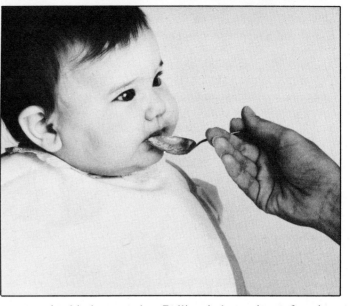

The end of this month marks your baby's half-year birthday, and he is now right in the middle of one of the most exciting periods of infancy. When the frustrations of learning to become mobile aren't bothering him too much, he is almost chronically in a good mood.

At about this time the considerable difference in behavior among babies becomes increasingly evident. Each tends to focus temporarily on one particular area of development. One baby concentrates on trying to creep; another works hardest on his vocal skills; still another spends long hours studying the minute details of his playthings, perhaps comparing one with another. One thing is certain: every baby is very busy at *something*.

Throughout the coming weeks and months, the focus will change from time to time until eventually most babies will have "caught up" with each other. In other words, sooner or later every baby really does learn to walk and talk. Parents' excitement about their baby often makes them impatient for the next behavioral step to be accomplished. There may be competition (subconscious, we hope) with other parents about whose baby is doing what first, but this only results in needless worry and frustration for some parents, which may show in the way they handle their baby.

Even the baby who appears to spend a great portion of his waking hours "just looking" is nevertheless still learning and growing. He is absorbing much more visual stimuli than babies who are intent on something else. When your baby is ready, he will sit and crawl and stand. He may be doing all of those things by the end of this month, or he may begin them during other months. Enjoy his achievements and look forward without concern to those yet to come.

Nobody has to teach a baby how to move across the floor. His innate curiosity prompts him to investigate new worlds; his growing independence prompts him to do it by himself. This month your baby may well begin creeping (that is, with his abdomen still on the floor), but he probably isn't yet ready for crawling on hands and knees (with abdomen off the floor*). He probably navigates backward before he goes forward. After all, in the beginning it's difficult enough just to remember which arm or leg to move next. Occasionally a baby will discover a different technique: for example, by lifting his head and bottom, he may be able to draw both knees up under him and flop forward. It's not a terribly practical method, but it does manage to get him from one spot to another.

Baby's main strength is still in his arms, but you will notice him performing push-ups and any number of other maneuvers

For whatever obscure reason, some childhood authorities apply these terms with the reverse meaning. Webster's Dictionary offers no helpful distinction between the two. We therefore use the terms here as defined by many prominent pediatricians, including T. Berry Brazelton, M.D., Chief of the Child Development Unit, Children's Hospital Medical Center in Boston.

to exercise his leg muscles. Rolling is becoming a favorite sport. Once baby has learned to turn from his stomach to his back, he may delight in rolling from one end of the room to the other. From time to time howling cries will beckon you to extract him from a too-tight spot. Usually you will find him wedged under a chair or between two pieces of furniture, but you'll be amazed at the inconceivable places he will occasionally manage to fit into.

By the end of the sixth month, many babies are able to sit alone although they probably won't be able to get into position by themselves. Most babies can easily sit for half an hour with some support. (If your baby tends to slump sideways or forward, she's not ready yet.) At first baby will keep her hands available to lend assistance if needed, but later on she will sit in the middle of the floor or crib holding toys in both hands, just as she did before she sat alone.

Your baby is probably thoroughly enjoying his bouncer or walker now, but a few babies just don't like it at all, much to mother's distress. A baby who does enjoy it will often remain happily content for as long as two hours, alternately exercising and playing with his toys. He is thrilled to be able to so easily view the world from what scientists refer to as vertical orientation. Now he looks across the room and out a window to see entirely new and different vistas from when he was flat on his back. Such walkers are excellent for stimulating the leg extensor reflex but must be used with caution: suddenly baby can maneuver over to all kinds of unsafe places.

Before long baby will discover that he can inch his bouncer across the floor if he moves in just the right way. He may feel confident enough to even stand up occasionally, first holding on with both hands, later with just one. For decades scientists have argued whether baby's urge to stand represents an inborn desire or whether it is simply imitative of the people he sees around him. Probably both answers are partially correct, but we do know that nothing can stop a baby from standing up and walking once the urge comes to him.

Nevertheless, once baby's urge to stand becomes a reality, he automatically becomes more accident prone. Coupled with his desire to reach out for any object that attracts his attention, is the danger that he might fall out of his highchair or carriage. *Before* he—and you—have a real scare is the time to begin using a baby harness. Many new parents are reluctant to use a harness, feeling that such contraptions are suitable only for animals, but they find their opinions rapidly changing with baby's first near-miss at toppling overboard.

Baby has apparently concluded that dressing and diapering are his special times to practice sitting up or to work on his leg exercises. Probably the best aid (there is no real solution) is one or two special toys to distract him. A music box, particularly if the working mechanism is visible, usually intrigues him. You will think of others, but they should be reserved specifically for the dressing table or they're sure to lose their appeal.

Eating provides heightened interest for baby now that he is beginning to manipulate some of his own food. He likes to feed himself a slice of toast or piece of banana, for instance. (If he chokes on any such foods, wait another week or two and try again.) But all foods, whether the do-it-yourself variety or the kinds you are feeding him, have become an adventure. Baby not only wants to taste and smell but also to squeeze, crumble, mash and smear. At least one child psychologist recommends that this is the age to begin teaching neatness by keeping a washcloth handy for carefully wiping face, hands and high-chair tray after each bite.

Whether you are breast- or bottle-feeding, your pediatrician may now suggest that you switch your baby to cow's milk. Some doctors recommend this at an earlier age, but since cow's milk is high in protein and salt, it places an increased load on the infant's kidneys and is therefore not recommended until the age of six months or later.

Constipation often becomes a problem for your baby after he begins drinking cow's milk because it is lower in carbohydrates. Protein forms a much harder curd and may be difficult for the immature digestive system to handle well. If constipation occurs, your pediatrician will probably recommend either increasing the amount of fruit your baby gets or starting fruits at this time if baby is not already eating them.

As your baby begins to really enjoy some of the solids he is eating, he may become less and less interested in his milk, particularly if he has just switched to the less-sweet cow's milk. Milk may even become the least liked food, in which case it may become necessary to give him his milk before his solids for a while.

About this time your baby is just beginning to show some signs of primitive planning in his exploratory behavior rather than merely confining himself to an immediate response. This new intellectual activity is part of what motivates him to begin creeping. A good deal of his maneuvering is performed with a definite goal in mind: a toy to reach or a footstool to explore, for example.

Reaching, grabbing, holding and tugging are becoming better coordinated. But baby's biggest problem with these skills is that he doesn't really know how to let go yet. As he continues to practice transferring an object from hand to hand, he will gradually learn the concept of deliberate release.

Your baby is now becoming fascinated with small particles such as crumbs on his highchair tray or specks of lint on the rug. He tries to pick them up but is rarely successful since he uses his whole hand for the task. Larger objects he can manipulate well now. He may hold two similar items together, turning them in his hands and comparing them. By the end of the month, he may try to stack one block on top of another if he watches you do it first and there is nothing else happening to distract him.

Your baby shakes almost everything he picks up and finds that some things make noise and some don't. Eventually he will learn from this that it is the *object* that makes the noise, but right now he persists with the notion that his hand is making it. He bangs toys together or against the floor, crib or bouncer and compares their sounds. He drops them to the floor—over and over again—partly to listen to the different noises they make, partly to see if they always do the same things each time they fall. He objects loudly if the toys are not immediately retrieved for him or if one is taken away. This all adds up to frustrating activity for mother, but it is very necessary for baby, and he enjoys every second of it.

Now that your baby is becoming mobile you want to be sure that he has safe places to play. While stairway gates and radiator guards are obvious safety measures (if your home has stairs and hot radiators), there are numerous less obvious dangers. Double-check appliance cords, and examine floors and baseboards for loose nailheads or splintered areas. If you haven't already done so, put caps over all unused electrical outlets (available at any hardware store, among other places). Low shelving may have sharp corners that can collide uncomfortably with baby's head. (Try taping a padded bandage over the corner for the next two or three months, even though at least a few visitors are sure to ask you what your baby has done to "injure" the shelf.) Make every effort to keep small, sharp objects off the floor. If there is an older child in the family, this can become a real problem unless you enlist his or her aid. (Sometimes dubbing the sibling Official Floor Inspector will help.) Babies have an uncanny and very imaginative ability to discover sources of mischief and potential danger.

Once your baby becomes more courageous in his expeditions to other parts of the house, you will need to check him every few minutes. But don't hover. The idea is to provide your baby with the safest, least restrictive environment possible, and then let him explore by himself.

Just about anything becomes a toy at this age, as long as it won't harm your baby (and vice versa). Giving him only a few things to play with at a time enables you to renew the supply every little while so that he doesn't become bored.

A length of rubber or plastic tubing about two feet long can be captivating as baby curves it into loops and any number of other shapes. During a fussy period away from home, your key ring is a quickly available diversion, but use caution—when baby tires of it he'll simply drop it. No one toy remains interesting for very long at one time, but the fact that baby is so distractible is what helps to keep him manageable.

The changing shapes of a turning mobile or leaves on a tree are puzzling to your baby. He is not always sure whether the movement indicates an animate or inanimate object, and he may happily strike up a dialogue with a tinkling windchime. He babbles a great deal and is learning to express different emotions. Although basically he is still limited to pleasure, expressed vocally as "dada," and complaint, expressed vocally as "mamamama," he is beginning to demonstrate other feelings as well. He is gaining an understanding of speech by the tone of voice that is used and responds with a different facial expression according to whether the voice sounds angry, comforting or approving.

Charles Darwin, so well-known for his *Origin of Species,* also authored considerable work on the expression of emotions. In his "Biographical Sketch of an Infant" (c. 1877), he wrote that his six-month-old son "assumed a melancholy expression, with the corners of his mouth turned down, when his nurse pretended to cry." That was considered a rather imaginative observation at the time, but researchers today know that such reactions are not uncommon at this age.

This is also a time of abrupt mood changes, wholehearted and undisguised. Baby may display his temper when something doesn't suit him and may be just as quickly calmed by a distracting toy. After another month or so, this abruptness will become a little less obvious as baby very, very slowly begins to gain a bit of control over his feelings. Don't expect too much, though. This is a process that continues at least into the preschool years.

Your baby can't follow you when you leave the room, and he can't remember your face until it reappears again. But he is now aware of your presence by the sounds you make as you busy yourself in other parts of the house. He will try to attract your attention frequently, either vocally or by some other means. And, of course, he expects you to answer.

Baby is beginning to build up a passive vocabulary, a few words whose meanings she knows even though she is unable to use them herself. By the end of the month, she may respond by looking at one or two objects as you name them. This is really a milestone in speech development, even though it may appear quite unimpressive to the casual observer.

Your face now holds a new allure for your baby. He constantly studies it from different angles and wants to touch it at every opportunity. He pokes his fingers into your eyes, nose and mouth; he pulls your hair and ears and forgets to let go again. All of this is a bit disconcerting and perhaps uncomfortable for you, but it is baby's way of learning more about you. And again, he is testing the fact that you are really a separate person from him.

There is much time for interaction with other people now, and he will eagerly accept all offers to play from those he knows and feels comfortable with. But he will no longer smile at everybody. He is more selective now even though he enjoys socializing.

He will probably enjoy a little roughhousing and may squeal with delight when swooped high in the air. Some babies are terrified of being lifted so high, however, and this has nothing to do with physical prowess or intellectual attributes. So respect his wishes and don't try to "teach" him to enjoy it.

Games like peekaboo become increasingly more fun for baby, even though she still isn't ready for anything but passive participation. She is, however, also gaining a sense of security about loved ones who "disappear" and then return almost immediately as though she had willed it.

The question often arises as to what extent a parent should be involved in baby's learning activities and physical development. The answer is simple: whenever and as long as both you and baby are enjoying what you're doing together. There are a number of books available that purport to teach you how to raise your baby's I Q level. Some of these books may offer some interesting ideas for you and baby. But one or two words of caution are in order: first, watch for *signs* that baby is ready to learn a new activity; don't go by the chronological ages indicated in the book. Second, don't take *any* of these books so seriously that you forget to enjoy what you're doing. And third, don't let their authors cause you to feel guilty because you're not knocking yourself out to keep your baby two weeks "ahead" of your best friend's baby.

The end of the first half year is a time when mothers (and fathers) tend to become almost obsessed with comparisons. If your baby is already sitting alone, there will be predictions that he will be walking early. The fact is that he may or may not walk early, and there is certainly no reason for you to feel obligated to "help" him walk early. Ten years from now it won't make any difference whether he began walking at nine months or fifteen months. One ten-year-old doesn't walk any better than another just because he started sooner. Relax.

development chart

PHYSICAL	SENSORYMOTOR	INTELLECTUAL	SOCIAL
Turns and twists in all directions.	Holds one block, reaches for a second and looks at third.	Remains alert two hours at a time.	Prefers play with people, especially cooperative games.
Can roll from back to stomach.	Reaches to grab and secure dropped object.	Inspects objects for a long time.	Babbles and becomes active during exciting sounds. Babbles back more in response to female voices (higher pitch).
May get up on hands and knees in crouch, hurtle forward or backward by flinging out arms and legs.	Coos or hums or stops crying in response to music.	Reaches quickly and without jerkiness for anything he sees.	Vocalizes pleasure and displeasure; grunts, growls or complains; coos, gurgles with pleasure; squeals with excitement; giggles, belly laughs.
Creeps by propelling self on stomach with legs and steering with arms; may go forward or backward.	Likes to play with food. Some interest in finger-feeding self.	Eyes now direct hands for reaching.	
Turns head freely.	Develops strong taste preferences.	Likes to look at objects upside down and create changes in perspective.	Tries to imitate facial expression.
Balances well when sitting; can lean forward or to one side.	May start manipulating cup and holding by handle.	May compare two objects.	Turns when hears own name.
Sits in chair and bounces or grasps dangling object.	Rotates wrist to turn and manipulate objects.	Has abrupt mood changes and different emotions; primary moods are pleasure, complaint and temper.	Disturbed by strangers. Smiles at mirror image.
Sits alone momentarily; may sit unsupported up to half an hour.	Often reaches with one arm instead of both.	Can utter more consonants (f, v, th, s, sh, z, m, n). Varies volume, pitch and rate of utterance.	
While rolling from back to side, may bend self nearly into a sitting position.	Sleeps through the night.		

Note: These charts are to be regarded as guidelines only. Many babies will perform each activity earlier or later than indicated.

Baby is now using his hands to imitate actions he has seen others do. He may clap his hands or make a fist or try to clean his highchair tray with a sponge.

The third quarter of baby's first year is a thrilling period. To say merely that it is a time of rapid growth is to imply that the months up to now have not been, which is obviously far from the truth. But in view of your baby's upcoming accomplishments, it is almost as though the first half-year has been a training period for active duty.

During the next three months, your baby will become increasingly mobile. No longer will he be compelled to wait for mother to go to him; now he can go to her. Great strides in baby's thought and language development become readily apparent. His advances in both motor and mental skills together lead him toward rudimentary problem solving.

Your baby's world is enlarging. By the end of this month, he will most likely be crawling or creeping—or will have figured out some way of getting himself from here to there. He is doing a lot of playing without toys now and is inclined to giggle a lot. Much of the frustration that preceded creeping may be over for a while, although in a few active babies it may quickly reappear in a determined effort to stand and walk a few steps. But frustration is a necessary part of learning. It provides necessary motivation for baby to reach new goals.

Your baby is probably sitting well without support now. A few babies may be able to assume the sitting position by themselves, but most cannot keep from falling over again in the process. At first, while your baby is sitting, he will use his hands mainly as props to keep himself from tipping over. By the end of the month, however, his balance will have increased considerably, and he will begin to combine sitting with other activities. He will sit and handle a toy, for example, and as soon as he feels brave enough, he will reach out for another.

Each baby develops his own way of moving across a room. If you were to try to teach him your idea of "a better way," it would be a difficult lesson to deliver. Even first-hand demonstration wouldn't be of much help.

Last month your baby was busily strengthening muscles, almost as though he knew instinctively that crawling requires the use of almost every muscle in the body. You probably witnessed his powerful leg thrusts. At diaper changes you watched his back arch as he lay with his face up but looking far back for an upside-down view of his surroundings.

Now most babies have raised themselves to hands and knees; soon they will begin to sway back and forth; before long a tentative hand or a knee will reach out. As practice continues, hands and knees will gradually coordinate enough to become a real crawl. And although he may start in a backward direction, baby will quickly learn to readjust his movements. A few more days and you'll be marveling at his speed. The race is on!

But we have not been talking about *all* babies. Some develop other styles of navigating that may occur either before, after or instead of the creeping stage. One baby may propel himself along on his side; another may develop a backstroke maneuver.

When he is strong enough for crawling, he may try it leapfrog style with both hands together followed by both knees, rather than the classic right hand/right knee followed by left hand/left knee. Still other babies prefer to remain upright and scoot along on their behinds. They may change to a crawling pattern later, but a few never do.

Whatever the method, baby leaves in his wake a trail of disorder. He is gaining a concept of distance as he sets out on each expedition. But there are many distractions. There are sounds to stop and listen to. There are books to be pulled from low shelves. There are toys to scatter and the newspaper to take apart. With so much to be done, it's no wonder baby is both physically and emotionally exhausted by naptime.

Curiosity vies with fear. Baby wants to explore the room on the other side of that doorway, but you are here and he doesn't want to leave you. Eventually he conquers his uncertainties and plunges through—but not for long. He quickly returns to touch base with you. Safely refueled he's off again, for a little longer this time. But every little while he's back to check on you and is devastated if you have disappeared. If you have very roomy living quarters and tend to move around a lot, it's a good idea to let your baby know where you are every few minutes so he won't worry too much.

There aren't likely to be any major changes in sleeping habits at this time. Some babies may sleep better after the exhaustion of the day while others may have become overtired and tend to wake more than usual during the night. Wait to see if baby settles back to sleep by himself. If not, brief reassurance is the most that is required from you. After the first half-year, sickness and travel tend to be more disruptive to your baby's sleep than before. You might as well muster up some extra patience because it may take several days for baby to readjust to his usual routine.

Your baby has probably moved into the big tub for bathtime now. Only a few inches of water are needed: a bathtub is a slippery place for a soapy baby. Playing in the tub water is a favorite pastime. An eggbeater is great fun, along with funnels, strainers, measuring cups and a baster—if it isn't too difficult for baby to squeeze. Suspend a net bag from the towel rack nearest the tub for storing the bath playthings. The toys can easily drip into the tub and dry, yet they're out of the way for those in the family who may not feel like bathing in the company of a rubber duck and a fleet of plastic boats.

Your baby probably has one or two teeth by now. Usually the lower incisors are the first to appear, but not always. Unusual teething patterns tend to run in families, however, so there is a certain amount of predictability here. Baby continues to enjoy eating and experimenting with finger foods. Handing him a cracker or teething biscuit to hold while you feed him his regular solids may help to keep at least one hand out of the spoon. Use caution in giving him finger foods between meals, however. They serve nicely to quiet a fussy baby, but they can also become part of bad eating habits that aren't so easily broken later on. Babies (and young children) have very small stomachs. There just isn't room for them to eat between meals and at mealtime, too, without becoming overweight.

Parents often wonder what time of day is best for serving baby's main meal. It really doesn't matter from a nutritional standpoint. But until baby's diet becomes more varied, his meat and vegetable meal is probably best offered in the middle of the day. In the evening many parents find that dinner goes most smoothly if baby is fed first and then allowed to join the rest of the family with a piece of toast to chew on in his highchair. It all depends on the baby, however. You may find it more relaxing to eat dinner after baby is tucked in for the night.

While your baby may enjoy feeding himself foods that he can hold in his hands, he may balk at those you are feeding him, either because he doesn't like the taste or because he wants to do it himself. Try as he might, he is simply not dexterous enough yet to fit a spoon into his mouth with any regularity. Mothers worry, of course, if baby isn't eating exactly what the pediatrician says he should be eating. There rarely is any need for concern. If your baby is receiving a multi-vitamin preparation, his other daily nutritional needs are very few: one pint (16 ounces) of milk, perhaps varied with occasional use of yogurt; an ounce of fresh fruit or half a jar of baby fruit; and half a jar of baby meat or other iron-containing protein suggested by your pediatrician. Even without a vitamin supplement, baby's only additional requirement is a serving (about one-third jar) of baby vegetable, alternating green and yellow vegetables every two or three days.

It is difficult to avoid getting that amount of food into your baby. Don't feel you can just forget about all the other items on his daily menu, though. We have listed only the basic *nutritional* requirements; your baby has calorie requirements as well. Ideally, the balance of his calories should come from as great a variety of foods as possible, but it's not strictly necessary at this age. Right now it's more important for baby to realize that eating is an enjoyable pastime. Continue to offer new foods regularly. You can urge him to taste, but *don't* urge him to "clean up his plate" or to eat something he obviously detests. When he loses interest and starts to squirm, he's telling you that he's had enough.

A baby can become bored with the bottle at this age. If she's taking milk fairly well from a cup, she *may* be ready to give up one or two bottles a day. But don't hurry it! Most babies aren't ready for weaning until near the end of the first year. They still need to suck, and there is no advantage in creating frustrations that could very well turn into behavior problems later on, if not immediately.

It isn't a good idea to allow your baby to take his bottle to bed with him, either at night or naptime, even though he now prefers to hold it himself. In addition to the possibility of psychological dependence, there is a sound physical reason for this. The milk can adhere to the teeth, promoting a distinctive type of tooth decay called "nursing bottle syndrome."

We mentioned before that playing with the ears is a common symptom of teething. This may become increasingly prevalent now. A great many babies also suck the lower lip when they're teething. The teething process does appear to cause some babies to suffer considerably more than others, but if there is really a great deal of discomfort, you should look for other causes. Too often teething unjustly becomes a catchall explanation for any unusual behavior. While it can cause a low-grade fever and some change in bowel movements, teething does not cause high fever or diarrhea, so don't make the mistake of ignoring actual illness by assuming that baby is "just teething."

Toe-sucking sometimes worries mothers simply because it seems to them an unsanitary sort of habit. Actually toes are just as clean as fingers until your baby is old enough to be walking around outdoors without shoes (by which time he will no longer be interested in sucking his toes anyway). Recent studies by Dr. Harvey Kravitz, professor of pediatrics at Northwestern University Medical School and Children's Memorial Hospital in Chicago, reveal that toe-sucking occurs in 83 percent of all normal infants, usually between the ages of six and seven months. If the habit were anything to be alarmed about, at least it would be a near-universal problem.

There will be occasions, during dinner preparations, for instance, when you cannot watch your baby closely. Those are times for the play yard. But otherwise baby needs the freedom to conduct what Ira J. Gordon in *Baby to Parent, Parent to Baby* refers to as "environmental engineering." Psychologically and intellectually baby needs to understand his environment. His engineering tactics help him learn something about the essence of the things around him. Concepts so familiar to adults that we no longer even think about them are still new to baby. For example, he discovers that there must be something under a chair to hold it up and that some chairs have four legs while others may have a pedestal, and still others have tiny legs and a lot of springy padding. Some chairs move back and forth; some turn around; and most don't move at all—wondrous revelations to the novice explorer!

Your baby's ability to grasp objects is becoming more sophisticated. Now he is beginning to use his fingers rather than the palms of his hands. He continues to pass objects from hand to hand, and everything reachable must be lifted, shaken, banged, poked, pushed, squeezed, rolled and thrown.

Cause and effect associations are becoming more realistic. Last month if you happened to turn on his light as he was scratching the sides of his crib, he was likely to conclude that his scratching magically caused the light to go on. Now, assuming that he has had the opportunity to operate the light switch, he is able to form a more scientific conclusion. (Of course, to baby there is still a certain amount of "magic" involved, but at least he recognizes a realistic relationship.)

Baby is now using his hands to imitate actions he has seen others do. He may clap his hands or make a fist, for instance, and may try to clean his highchair tray with a sponge just the way you do. Handedness may or may not be present at this time, but during the next month or two, four out of five babies will exhibit a definite preference for the right hand. Almost every parent and educator today is aware of the dangers of attempting to change a child's handedness. For years parents were warned that when offering a toy or cup to baby, it should be held directly in front of him so that he could reach for it with either hand. Then along came the theory that there is a crucial time in baby's development when hand dominance occurs and that if objects are always held toward his right hand, that is the one he will probably become more accustomed to using. The trouble with this theory is that there is no valid means of proving it. Left-handedness is not a handicap.

Vocalizing is still extensive except for those short periods of time when some babies are concentrating hard on learning new motor activities. Pleasure is indicated by a wide range of sounds, all the way from soft cooing to raucous crowing. Baby makes frequent attempts to mimic the sounds uttered to him by an adult, and he is learning the meaning of "no" by the tone of your voice.

Playthings for this age are little different from those of previous months except that your baby will probably be doing different kinds of things with some of them. If the season is right, a wading pool is great fun now. Your baby will probably enjoy looking at magazines and picture books with you, but he is also learning that paper can be delightful in itself for the lovely crackling sound it makes.

Your baby has become more keenly aware of the continuing existence of things even though he cannot see them. He has already begun to search for an object that he dropped. Now he can recognize a familiar toy even though most of it is hidden behind a pillow, for example. Soon he will learn to search behind the pillow for a totally hidden object, if he has seen you put it there. He is also gaining a knowledge of the means-to-an-end principle. For instance, a toy lying on a nearby blanket may be out of reach. Baby will soon discover that although he cannot reach the toy, he can reach the blanket and that by pulling the blanket, he can bring the toy close enough to pick it up. Simple as these activities may seem, they represent milestones in baby's development.

You are still the focal point of your baby's life. He is learning even more about you by expanding his pulling and poking activities to now include biting and chewing—on your hair, your jewelry and your clothes. When he uses the term "mama," though, he probably isn't yet directing it specifically at you. He may just as likely be addressing another woman or voicing a complaint. A few more weeks and he will know that you, and only you, bear the label of his mama.

This is often a time when many mothers consider returning to work since they feel baby is so much less dependent now. Actually, your baby is still very dependent on you, but if you feel that for economic or other reasons you wish to return to your career, you should not feel guilty about it. Do take time for a careful selection of a caretaker for baby and for a gradual adjustment period. Most working mothers have found that the mother/baby relationship improves with this arrangement: when mother is at home, she can more easily devote undivided attention to her baby for a few hours a week. This is often more beneficial to baby than a mother who is too busy or preoccupied for such wholehearted interaction.

Roughhousing continues to be fun if it's not too near bedtime. It may have to be toned down a bit for a very active baby of this age, but it may help a quiet one to become a bit more sociable. In any case, after a busy day, your baby will appreciate winding up his activities with a few minutes of cuddling. It's still the best send-off for that trip to Sleepytown.

development chart

PHYSICAL	SENSORYMOTOR	INTELLECTUAL	SOCIAL
Pushes up on hands and knees and rocks back and forth. Creeps with an object in one or both hands; usually goes forward. May crawl (abdomen off floor). May move by raising and lowering buttocks while on back. Balances head well. Sits alone steadily for several minutes or more. Balances well and enjoys upright posture; hands no longer needed for support. May get self to sitting position by using arms to push up from side or by assuming crawl position and sticking legs out in front. May have two teeth.	Reaches for and grasps toy with one hand. Holds two objects simultaneously, one in each hand; may bang them together. Grasps, manipulates, mouths, bangs objects. Plays vigorously with noisemaking toys like bell, music box or rattle. Holds and manipulates a spoon or cup in play. Explores body with mouth and hands. Distinguishes near and far objects in space.	Attention more concentrated; greater interest in detail. Responds with expectation to repetition of event or of signal. Remembers small series of actions in immediate past if series includes his own actions. Begins to learn implications of familiar acts. May associate picture of baby with himself and give appropriate sound. Tries to imitate sounds or series of sounds. Has special, well-defined syllables (4 or more) but most vowels and consonants still occur at random. Most common sounds similar to ma, mu, da, di, ba. Vocalizes several sounds in one breath. May say "dada" and/or "mama" without meaning.	Shows desire to be included in social interaction. Wriggles in anticipation of play. Begins to show humor and teases. Resists pressure to do something he doesn't want to. May fear strangers. Reaches and pats at mirror image. Learning meaning of "no" by tone of voice.

Note: These charts are to be regarded as guidelines only. Many babies will perform each activity earlier or later than indicated.

You will witness what is unmistakably the process of conscious learning as baby tries out first one maneuver, then another.

This is the age of curiosity. Kittens, puppies, baby monkeys and young horses go through a similar stage, but for the human baby there is a difference. He has fewer instincts on which to rely.

The significance there is twofold: first, with little instinctive knowledge to guide him, the human baby must depend on *learned* knowledge—and there is so very, very much to begin accumulating. A baby of this age involves himself in a full-time job of exploring, examining, assimilating and storing his intellectual discoveries. But secondly, while he is doing all these things, he is almost without benefit of any instinctive awareness of danger, whether to himself or what he might cause to his surroundings. Even if animal instincts were still well developed in humans, they would have little relevance to the technological society in which we live.

And so the typical going-on-eight-months baby plows around the house blithely determined to further his education and, in the process, to rearrange the entire contents of his environment. Everything reachable must be moved, opened, emptied, banged, chewed, thrown and whatever else baby deems necessary at the moment. When restrictions are imposed, he becomes angry and insulted: how *dare* anyone intrude on his research of this great new three-dimensional world? When thwarted, he rages: when left to his own devices, his mood ranges from sober absorption to chortling glee.

Pediatricians like to tell the story about famous athlete Jim Thorpe's attempts to imitate a baby's every move for an entire day. After four hours Thorpe gave up in exhaustion while the baby merrily continued for an additional four hours. It's no wonder most mothers lapse daily into a state of fatigue from trying to keep up with their babies.

Undoubtedly your baby has been busily perfecting his crawling techniques and is becoming quite adept at moving around. Some babies are crawling so fast that they are difficult to keep track of except when they are following mother around the house. More than once baby will narrowly miss getting caught as you try to shut the bathroom door. Babies also love to park *behind* doors. Evidently they are so intrigued by the surprise element of a suddenly opening door that they're willing to accept a few knocks on the head. You'll have to use caution for a while when opening *and* closing doors. Babies also enjoy lying behind open doors and poking fingers through the crack between door and wall. It's easy to swing a door closed on a tiny finger if you're not extra careful.

Your baby is probably sitting well without support for considerable periods. She may be able to reach a sitting position by herself, but most of the time she'll be rather clumsy about it.

As crawling muscles strengthen, baby begins to use them in more frequent attempts to stand. Standing does not only depend on stronger legs, however. To pull oneself from prone to upright on both feet, requires some rather complicated

logistics. You will witness what is unmistakably the process of conscious learning as baby tries out first one maneuver, then another. He must figure out which hand goes where and how to shift his weight and when to move his legs. Each time he finds a way to raise himself a little higher, he will practice until the movement is perfected.

You cannot teach your baby to stand. If you try to help him, you'll probably find that his legs have become a pair of wet noodles. Baby needs to make his own mistakes until finally, through a long process of trial and error, he will find his own way up and be able to use it most efficiently. Once he's up, he will usually spend the next several weeks testing out what else he can do while he's up there. Baby will learn to hold with only one hand, how to support his weight on one leg, how to shift it to the other leg—all in preparation for his first walking steps. He learns just which objects or pieces of furniture are strong enough to support his weight and which are not. Soon he will discover he can lean against his support and leave both hands free for doing other things. Occasionally he succeeds in reaching a perpendicular position. But the exasperating part, for both baby and mother, is that it may be several more weeks before your baby can comfortably return to the floor. He will scream for you to help him down. When he does try to get down alone, his method is simply to let go. As he falls, he arches his back (the last remaining traces of the Moro reflex, according to some authorities), causing him to land flat, with a resounding knock on the head. It doesn't take much experimenting for baby to learn that this isn't a very functional means of returning to the ground.

While you can't teach your baby to stand, you *may* be able to show him how to bend forward from the waist so that when he goes down, he at least lands on the most padded part of his anatomy. Don't work too hard at it, though. It may become a game for him which he enjoys so much that he will delay looking for ways to get down on his own. When he finally does learn to go with ease in either direction, life will become a bit quieter for a while. You will see your baby practicing knee bends as he holds to his support with one hand and squats down to pick up a toy with the other. Finally, the business of standing comes under control.

Eating and sleeping patterns vary so much at this age that it's difficult to predict just what you're likely to encounter with your baby. Add to that the fact that patterns may vary from week to week, and you'll see that you might as well be ready to expect almost anything.

Some babies suddenly refuse to feed themselves anything at all but will willingly allow you to spoon it into them. Others may completely refuse the spoon but will cheerfully eat anything they can get their fingers around. Still others holler about baby food in any form but will eat whatever is on your plate. Sometimes for short periods, particularly when teething, babies seem to lose interest in eating any food but will spend long hours examining it.

Specific advice in this area is a bit skimpy, but if you allow yourself to get too uptight about mealtime, the result could be lingering feeding problems for your baby. What we do recommend is that you keep cool, follow your baby's wishes (within reason) and *do not* force-feed him. If he's enjoying the spoon, he'll want to help. That's all part of his ongoing research, not a subversive act of aggression, so you might as well let him carry on. He really doesn't understand why you should want to hold his hands out of the way. He may use his own spoon to feed you and takes a great deal of pleasure in being allowed to do so. (Don't worry about "germs"; you and baby undoubtedly share most, if not all, of the same ones anyway.) It probably doesn't hurt to let your baby have suitable bits of food from your own plate occasionally: some soup, soft-cooked vegetables, a taste of ice cream, for instance. But be careful not to give him anything he might choke on. A chicken bone with all splinters and meat removed is still tasty for a baby and will feel good when rubbed against sore gums.

Although a few babies (with lucky mothers) will continue taking two naps a day until they are fourteen or fifteen months old, most are already down to one nap a day by now. An active baby may sleep less than an average baby; on the other hand, he may tire himself to a point where he sleeps more than average.

Many of the frustrations of the day carry over into the sleeping hours, and your baby may again (or still) have waking periods in the middle of the night. The crib is a favorite place to practice standing, and this activity affords a perfect excuse to holler for help from mommy or daddy.

This is a time for firmness. Whether your baby wakes in the middle of the night or too early in the morning, he must be allowed to master sleep problems by himself now. But you will need to help him do that. No matter how much a baby fusses about going to bed at night, he should never be allowed to reach a state of frenzied exhaustion, which is almost guaranteed to interfere with restful sleep. A baby depends on his parents to make certain necessary decisions for him—both now and for many years to come. While noisy

protests may lead you to believe otherwise, your baby inwardly experiences relief that you have toned down his excitement.

You should realize, however, that half-hearted, maybe-decisions are worse than none at all. Baby senses your waverings so that instead of being helped by your guidance to feel more secure, he feels less so. Besides, your baby is becoming intelligent enough so that it won't take him long to realize that your indecision and lack of consistency have the effect of putting him in control. That doesn't mean you can't *ever* change your mind, of course. That kind of rigidity isn't logical either. But your baby requires a certain amount of order in his life, and to achieve that you should try to maintain effective and consistent guidance.

Your baby is now developing a pincer grasp, that is, the ability to pick up objects between thumb and forefinger. By the end of the month, he may be able to use his thumb and the very tip of his forefinger to pick up the crumbs and specks of lint that so intrigued him a month ago. This is really another kind of milestone because the opposed thumb is one of the distinguishing characteristics of humans. (It might be a good idea to remember this on the days when you suspect you have a wild animal lunging about the house rather than a human baby.)

Baby's entire reach/grasp/release mechanism is now better controlled. He no longer has to think quite so hard about what his hand is doing and can concentrate on the object itself. He will reach for just about anything, preferably objects that are about eight inches away. Reaching is one of the most fundamental ways your baby has of exploring the world. Once grasped, your baby is likely to put the object into his mouth or hold it a comfortable distance from his eyes and just look at it. He can also concentrate on the kind of repetitive banging that sets his mother's teeth on edge. He is learning to do different things with different kinds of playthings. Some favorites at this age are nesting cups, containers to fill with small objects, and simple dolls.

An all-time favorite place to play is the kitchen, partly because he has watched you "play" in it so often and partly because there are so many fascinating drawers and cupboards to explore—and empty. You will need to arrange your bottom cupboards so that they contain only safe unbreakables. You can try designating one special cupboard just for baby, but he won't be content with just one until he has thoroughly and frequently investigated all the others. If there are drawers you need to keep him out of, a yardstick or similar item can be slipped through the handle loops.

Wastebaskets hold special attraction for babies. They delight in emptying them, pawing through the contents and filling them up again. The trouble is that they don't always fill them up with the same things that came out of them. For the next several months, you'll have to carefully check through your baskets before permanently disposing of the waste. Every once in a while you'll be glad you took the trouble to do it. Conversely, you will also need to be a bit more careful about what you leave in the wastebasket. Baby can make a royal mess with just a single sheet of carbon paper. Tiny, sharp items, such as the pins or staples from clothing tags, present a special danger right now and should be disposed of where baby cannot get to them.

Your baby may now be able to point to something she wants, and with her eyes she can follow an object you may wish to point out to her. Her eyesight and attention to detail are so great that she can pick out a single new object in a room. (It isn't always something you are eager for her to find, so watch where you set things down.)

Language development is taking place long before a baby learns to talk. Keep chatting with him; he is listening more closely now. As much of the time as possible, use simple, concrete ideas. Baby still has no comprehension whatsoever of abstract concepts, but he is aware of sound, rhythms and is picking up a word here and there. You can have fun with a tape recorder now if you can turn it on without attracting baby's attention at a time when he is happily talking to himself. You will notice more frequent repetition of the syllables in words you use. Even what sound like "nonsense" syllables are probably his own versions of what he has been hearing but for which he hasn't yet learned to make the correct letter sounds. (The letter "1," for instance, often cannot be pronounced until well after the age of two.)

A baby's ability to mimic often causes parents concern that their baby will pick up undesirable speech from a sitter who uses poor grammar, unusual speech patterns or a great deal of slang. You might wish to consider that aspect if you hire a full-time caretaker, but your baby is not likely to be very affected by the speech of a sitter he is with only sporadically. Neither national nor regional accents appear to have much effect on a baby's speech development, even when his own mother has a strong "foreign" accent. Traces of an accent that do creep into his speech usually disappear by the time he is two or three. (One exception here seems to be children whose mothers grew up in England. These babies do tend to learn and retain a somewhat British accent.)

An important point about language development that parents tend to forget is the noise level in their home or apartment. A baby has a difficult time trying to listen or practice talking if a TV or stereo is blasting nearby a good part of his day.

Along with your baby's growing ability for vocal mimicry is his newfound love for action mimicry. He's learning to wave, clap his hands and "answer" the telephone if he can reach it. Whether it has rung or not, the phone is a pretty interesting gadget: unlike most toys it makes different kinds of noises depending on what one does to it. If you have one of the fancier models that plays a tune as you push buttons instead of dial, you'll have a difficult time separating baby from telephone. At the time of this writing, telephone technology has yet to develop a babyproof phone (proof, perhaps, that babies are intrinsically smarter than electronic engineers?). Until it does, you will again have to apply firmness. You can try moving the telephone(s) out of reach, but that will only be a temporary deterrent.

Stranger anxiety may be better or worse than it has been during the last month or two. Sometimes at this age a fear of strangers becomes more intense when baby isn't feeling well or is grumpy from having just wakened. Generally speaking, he "knows" more people now and is beginning to feel less threatened. If the stranger doesn't approach too rapidly, baby may even agree to be held in his or her arms as long as his mother or father remains in the same room.

If you communicate trust in persons who are close to you but are "strangers" to baby—such as grandparents, friends and neighbors—baby will eventually learn to feel the same kind of trust. He will continue to dislike eye-to-eye contact with them, however; he cannot yet cope with that much intimacy.

Even though babies are wary of strangers at this age, they continue to accept friendly overtures from young children—a phenomenon we mentioned in an earlier chapter. Moreover,

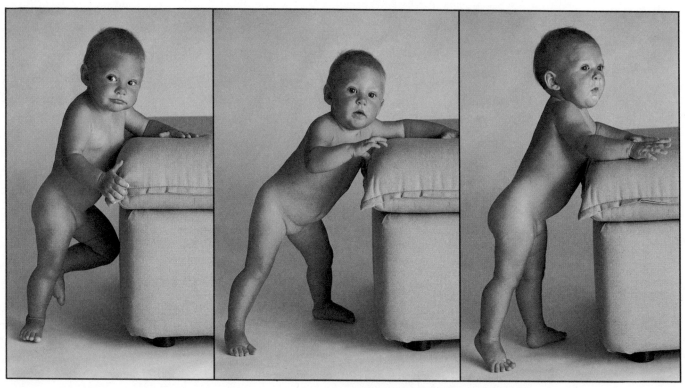

careful studies have shown that a baby relates more easily to others of his own sex.

In spite of other kinds of fears, it is highly unlikely that your baby is afraid of a car. The opposite is probably true, especially now that he can sit up in his car seat and has so much to look at through the windows. Be sure that he is able to see easily. The seat should be well-padded and constructed in such a way that even the most active baby cannot work it loose from its position.

A footnote for exasperated mothers: about this time most mothers tend to become even more frustrated than their babies as they secretly (or not so secretly) wish that baby would hurry and start moving around by himself more easily and without turning the whole house upside down, and that he would stop throwing food all over the place and learn to talk so that communication would be less of a guessing game. It's understandable. On particularly fussy days you can't help wondering at least once an hour if it will ever end.

If there is an older child in the family, sibling rivalry may become more of a problem about this time. The novelty of a new baby in the family has worn thin, and baby is perceived as more of a threat. In spite of careful preparation, it is not uncommon for a preschooler to now inquire as to when the baby will be returned to the hospital (or the store). Exhausting as it may be, try to adhere to your older child's previous schedule of activities as much as possible.

Remember that in spite of new achievements, your baby is still little and still vulnerable. Keep taking an occasional look at baby's world from his point of view. It will perhaps help you to better understand the goals he is reaching for as he perpetrates one mess after another. Babies simply don't organize into the same categories that adults use. In *Your Baby's Mind and How It Grows*, Dr. Mary Ann Spencer Pulaski states that objects are classified into what is "movable...eatable...touchable." It's a grand, exciting universe for baby, and his own frustrations provide the necessary stimulation for acquiring new skills and knowledge. Much of baby's fussiness is simply an indicator of how hard he is struggling to grow up.

Throughout the rest of the first year, you will notice almost daily changes in your baby, however trivial they may be. There will be bad moments to be coped with, but there will also be many joys to treasure. Some days it's just easier to forget about whatever it is you're trying to do and spend some extra time with baby. After all, you will never again have the opportunity to interact in the same way with *this* baby at *this* age.

development chart

PHYSICAL	SENSORYMOTOR	INTELLECTUAL	SOCIAL
Crawls, either forward or backward at first.	Examines objects as external, 3-dimensional realities.	Recalls past event and past action of his own.	Shouts for attention.
Sways on knees.	Watches hands in various positions, holding and dropping objects.	Retains small series of events in immediate past.	May know how to use parents to get things for him.
May crawl with object in one hand.		Anticipates events independent of his own behavior.	Sustains interest in play.
Pivots on stomach.	Holds and manipulates one object while watching second object.	Begins to show memory of timing.	Enjoys games such as "so big" and "catch me."
Sits alone steadily for several minutes.		Has mental model of human face and is becoming interested in its variations.	May wave bye-bye.
Can sit and bounce on buttocks.	Thumb, first and second fingers grasp an object like a block.		Babbles with variety of sounds and inflections, alone or with others. Uses adult intonations when babbling.
Stands with hands free while leaning against something.	Developing pincer grasp with thumb and forefinger.	Begins imitating people and behaviors out of sight and earshot.	Begins to mimic mouth and jaw movements.
Uses furniture to pull himself to standing position.	Can pick up string.	Can solve simple problems like kicking at a hanging toy to try to get it.	Pushes away something he doesn't want.
Needs help to get self down from standing.	Reaches for objects with fingers overextended.		Rejects confinement.
When held in standing position, puts one foot in front of the other.	Points and follows what someone else points to.	Begins establishing a learning style. Combines known bits of behavior into new act.	Fears strangers.
May have trouble sleeping.	Claps and waves hands.	Vocalizes in two syllables.	Is clearly attached to mother and fears separation from her.
	Tastes everything.	May say words "dada" and/or "mama" as specific names.	Pats, smiles at and tries to kiss mirror image.
		Listens selectively to familiar words and can recognize some.	Sibling rivalry a problem.

Note: These charts are to be regarded as guidelines only. Many babies will perform each activity earlier or later than indicated.

A curious baby is alert and independent, eager to add to his growing stores of knowledge. To do it effectively entails a great deal of messy research.

Depending on the degree of your baby's progress up to now, there may be a noticeable slowing down of major new accomplishments this month. But there is no slowing of the learning process or of baby himself. He is simply taking a little time out to practice, coordinate and perfect his skills. Details require further attention, and the databank may need some revisions. In other words, without anyone's having to prod him, your baby somehow senses he must consolidate what he has already learned before continuing on to the next step.

Curiosity is even more of a driving force now. If either you or your husband has a compulsion for neatness, you might as well resign yourself to giving it up for a little while. A curious baby is alert and independent, eager to add to his growing stores of knowledge. To do it effectively entails a great deal of messy research.

Your young perpetual motion machine is becoming ever more mobile. He can probably raise himself to a sitting position now and as with crawling, every baby has his own method. He may curl on his side and flip upright or pull his knees up under his stomach and flop backward onto his bottom. The variations are endless, and he will probably try out a number of them before he finds his own best way. From then on his waking hours will be spent in a tireless series of crawl/sit/examine, but with frequent trips back to home base to check on mother.

The urge to climb is a vestigial instinct still apparent in the human baby. Up is relatively easy for him; down can lead to disaster. Baby's growing intellect is combining with his physical ability to invent many kinds of climbing places, most of them somewhat less than safe. If, for instance, you have end tables with drawers, your baby may discover that by opening the drawers just so, he can climb on top of the table and from there to the sofa, where he promptly rolls to the floor. Until baby has mastered a more comfortable means of returning to firm ground, you will probably have to remove the drawers temporarily or turn the table so that the drawer pulls face the wall. That is only a single example. A clever baby will devise any number of other climbing challenges that the adult mind, focused on other levels, could not possibly conceive.

A very low footstool or similar item does afford a fairly safe means for baby's climbing and standing activities. If you have nothing that seems particularly appropriate, try to find a carton that is about six inches high. Filled with newspapers to keep it from tipping and then taped shut, it becomes excellent gymnastic equipment.

Many babies will be standing by the end of this month, with or without holding on to a support. An active baby will be able to stand alone, balancing well enough to play with a toy at the same time. Many will begin the process known as cruising, which could also be termed the pre-walking stage. Cruising usually begins as a trip up and down the length of the couch or around the coffee table. (You can worry about the fingerprints later; right now baby's enthusiasm is far more important.) As he becomes more adept, he will drift or flop from one piece of furniture to the next, alternately leaning or holding on with his hands. Depending on your furniture arrangement, he may be able to make it almost all the way around the room or even from one room to the next.

Some babies will try a tentative step or two between couch and chair or between chair and table. All babies will continue their climbing activities, and though they can't actually climb up a staircase yet, they can easily crawl to the top of it without any sense of how to get back down. It's a good idea to make the stairs off-limits for a while.

Grasping and manipulating are much more advanced than in previous months, and baby can now grasp tiny objects between his thumb and forefinger with precision. He can also accommodate his hand to the shape of the object he is reaching for.

A baby's drooling has almost disappeared by now, which many mothers take as an indication for weaning. Scientifically there is no correlation. The decreased drooling is simply another sign of baby's growing physical maturity.

If you have been breast-feeding, however, this may be a suitable time for you to consider weaning. Usually by this age a breast-feeding baby has had more than sufficient sucking and cuddling satisfaction and is ready to make the big break to the cup. Your pediatrician will advise you how to proceed.

Keep in mind that even though your baby may be showing less interest in his breast-feedings, he will still miss your closeness very much for a while. He will probably clamber over to nestle on your lap at frequent intervals and should be encouraged to do so. This can be a disconcerting time for many mothers. You may have thought you could hardly wait until your baby was ready to leave the breast, only to discover afterwards how much you miss the experience. Nevertheless, this is part of your baby's growing-up process.

If you have been bottle-feeding and your baby shows a distinct lack of interest in the bottle, you *might* consider weaning at this time. At about nine months many babies indicate a readiness for weaning though they will probably change their minds next month. This readiness tends to reappear at about one year, however, so you don't have to feel this is your last chance.

If you are considering weaning at this time, check with your pediatrician first, not only about the procedure but also to see whether he feels your baby is ready for it. He may tell you that this is too early for baby's best adjustment. In any case weaning really should be your *baby's* decision—in spite of what other mothers are telling you about how early their own babies were weaned. The emphasis on earliness throughout every step of childhood is almost unique to the American culture. Dr. T. Berry Brazelton writes about American mothers in *Infants and Mothers*: "Each is ready to help another feel inadequate as a mother."

There is absolutely no need to rush a baby away from his bottle before he is ready, and there is no harm in his continuing with it into the second year. As long as you don't make an issue of it and baby's emotional needs are being met in other ways, he will simply tire of it one day.

You might keep one point in mind, however. A baby who has been feeding herself the bottle will have more difficulty giving it up than if you have been doing it. Part of her readiness to give up the bottle is due to her readiness to give up *you* as she becomes more independent. If the association isn't there, she will still give up you but not necessarily the bottle. If you feel this will bother you, you probably should at least hold baby on your lap at bottle time, even though she will probably insist on handling the bottle herself.

Along similar lines of too-early weaning is too-early toilet training. Incredible as it may seem, a current child development book advocates starting toilet training at the age of eight or nine months. (We hasten to add that although the book was written by a well-known baby expert, he neither lives nor works in the United States.) With perhaps a very, very rare exception, every pediatrician in the country will tell you that no baby of this age can be trained; only the mother can be trained to "catch" him at the right time.

It is sheer nonsense to suppose that a baby of eight or nine months will willingly surrender from his exciting, busy day the number of hours necessary to attempt such early training. He doesn't have a clue as to what you want of him, and after the first trip or two, he isn't particularly interested. Even if he did want to cooperate, he will not have enough muscle control for about another year.

Teeth-grinding, assuming baby now has enough teeth to grind, often begins about this age and occurs especially at night. It is a form of tension release that may be associated with cutting new teeth. (It used to be thought that teeth grinding indicated worms, but this does not appear to be the case in infants.) The habit is not in the least bit harmful—it just sounds that way—and will be outgrown in due time.

Head-banging occurs in about seven percent of all normal babies and is three to four times more common among boys than girls. A large number of head-bangers are also body-rockers, and medical science has yet to offer either cause or cure. Studies disclose no correlation between head-banging and either mental retardation or a disturbed relationship with baby's parents. The same studies of head-bangers reveal normal brain waves and neither skull fractures nor brain injury. Alarming as head-banging may be to parents, serious head injuries very rarely occur, and the habit usually begins to wane about the middle of the third year.

A real concern is your baby's continuing safety. Now that he is possibly standing and will soon be walking, you will need to be still more careful about what your baby will be investigating next. It will soon be a simple matter for him to push a stool to the bathroom sink, where he can climb high enough to reach the medicine cabinet with its horde of disaster-producing substances. Even medications and toiletries intended for baby can become hazardous if ingested.

If your baby has gotten very active in her walker, stay near her when she is in it. Be aware of how far she can reach now, and be sure that anything dangerous is out of the way. A baby in a walker can usually use both hands to concoct his mischief, whereas a cruising baby must keep at least one hand available for holding on. (Be certain that you select a walker that is well-made. It should be extremely stable, sturdy and constructed so that fingers or chubby thighs will not be pinched.)

In addition to poisonous cleaning materials, the kitchen holds other sources of danger. Never leave any kind of knife or scissors within baby's reach. Unplug the toaster and all other small appliances when you're not using them. Pot handles must always be turned toward the wall (with or without a baby in the house). Watch the cord from your iron when you are ironing. Dry beans or peas can be pushed into tiny ears or up noses, where they swell and cause untold misery.

Your baby can now be taught the meaning of "hot" if you hold his hand high enough above a stove burner so that he feels the warmth as you say the word. Continue to repeat "hot," but louder, as you lower your own hand and quickly pull it back as if in pain. Baby will gradually get the idea and remember to avoid all stove burners.

In any part of the house, plants must be placed out of baby's reach. Not only can a heavy pot be pulled down on his head, but also parts of a surprising number of houseplants are poisonous if eaten. All baby furniture manufactured today is finished with lead-free paint, but this isn't necessarily true of other furniture or woodwork that baby might chew on. Your local health department can tell you how to go about having a painted item tested.

This danger list is far from complete. The idea is that you

must consider very carefully the many potential hazards in the average home and try at all costs to eliminate them from yours.

Increasing hand control and growing knowledge enable baby to begin applying to new situations what he has already learned elsewhere. He is forming an understanding of the relationship between certain objects. You will now see him fitting a lid on a pot or placing a plastic cup on its saucer. He can set an object more gently on a table. The first asymmetrical movement of his hands begins as he now holds an object in one hand and bangs with the other. Up to now he usually used both hands for the same operation.

Baby can now fit small objects through a hole in a larger one although he's not yet ready for sophisticated fitting toys. He can build a two-block tower and will often make several trips for a series of objects that he may be collecting and sorting.

Favorite new toys now include those with wheels on them. He will enjoy a drum and drumsticks but is just as happy banging on an old pot with a spoon. Be careful of granite cookware; it often chips easily.

Your baby will enjoy the oversized blocks made from heavy corrugated cardboard. They are surprisingly durable and inexpensive. Baskets and containers of all sorts are fun to fill up and empty again. Baby will especially like your giving him his own "mailbox"—any kind of box filled with discarded letters, old magazines and any other appropriate material.

If you notice your baby uttering certain syllables in connection with a particular object or situation, he is probably making his first attempts at speaking. For example, he may use "ba" for "bottle," and for now at least, that is sufficient for him. Although your baby will probably come out with one or

two real words in the next two or three months, he may not actually begin talking before the age of one and a half or even two. To their parents' astonishment, these "late starters" usually begin speaking in almost complete sentences.

What is far more important than baby's actual speech is his understanding of what is being said to him. Continue to talk to him in ordinary conversation, repeatedly identifying familiar objects or telling him what you're doing. Dr. Burton L. White, director of the Harvard University Preschool Project and author of *The First Three Years of Life*, has drawn up a list of the most commonly understood words between eight and twelve months. They include: mommy, daddy, names of other family members or pets, bye-bye, baby, shoe, ball, cookie, juice and no-no. In addition, most babies are beginning to understand simple instructions such as "wave bye-bye," "stop that," "come here," or "bring me…"

Your baby's understanding of the disappearance concept is increasing. He now really understands that people and objects have a separate existence when he cannot see them; that when you leave the room or the house, you have not disappeared forever. This concept has grown partly from his activities in putting little things into big things and covering them so they are out of sight. Similarly, games where you hide toys or other objects will contribute to his awareness. If, for instance, baby sees you hide a keychain behind a pillow, he will move the pillow and retrieve the keychain. However, if you then hide the keychain behind a second pillow, baby will again look behind the first pillow but not behind the second, even though he has watched your action. While his concept of disappearance is becoming more sophisticated, it obviously is not yet reliable.

Babies of this age love to play simple games with family members or others with whom they feel comfortable. A favorite is "so big." (For the uninitiated, in answer to "How big is the baby?" baby will hold his hand up somewhere in the vicinity of the top of his head.) Another is "catch me," as baby scrambles off with someone else in almost-hot pursuit. When he is finally "caught," he then becomes the chaser. Baby also likes guessing in which hand a tiny object is hidden; this is related somewhat to the disappearance concept just discussed.

Older brothers or sisters (three or more years older) usually enjoy playing these games with baby as much as adults do, and their patience usually lasts longer. There tends to be more extensive play between siblings now that there is so much more to do. But while the pleasure is increased, so is the fighting and competition. (Parents often complain that an older child hugs the baby until he cries—a clear-cut case of the ambivalent feelings prevailing at this age.)

Much more of what baby learns may also come from a big brother or sister. But while such a baby may be learning *more* than an only child would, he is probably learning less about the *process* of achievement. In other words, he is learning by imitation rather than by discovery. Siblings, like many adults, are intent on making sure that a toy is being used in the "right" way, and often, even unintentionally, they prevent baby from manipulating and discovering in his own way.

With or without older siblings, baby wants to be near his mother these days. He is thoroughly pleased with his new independence, but newness holds many of the same fears for him as it does for an adult. Baby wants to play in the same room with his mother much of the time and needs regular reassurance that everything is okay.

Reassurance is not the same as praise for every insignificant accomplishment, however. Praise is essential food for the soul but used indiscriminately, it loses its meaning. A great deal of what baby does is for the sheer joy of doing. Too much praise is confusing to him.

As much as baby wants and needs to be near his mother, father is still very special. The presence of father combines familiarity with novelty and adds immensely to baby's day. When allowed to baby-sit on a weekend afternoon, for instance, father tends to ignore routines and break a few rules. Of course, an occasional mischievous alliance is good for a baby. In an emergency, however, father can function just as effectively as mother—an ability that instills in baby feelings of both confidence and dismay.

This is also a time when other kinds of fears may begin to manifest themselves. The vacuum cleaner, an object to which your baby has shown no particular reaction, commonly causes an eight- or nine-month-old to scream in fright. Since you can't stop using the vacuum cleaner, you will need to reintroduce baby to the monster machine as gently as possible. Carry him with you for a few minutes as you vacuum. Hold him in your arms, and guide his hand to operate the on-off button to help him build the awareness that it is you and he who are in control, rather than the machine.

Either now or in later months your baby may express panic when you let the water out of the bathtub. Whether it is the peculiar noise, the disappearance of the water, or (as has often been proposed by psychologists) a baby's fear that he might wash down the drain along with the water, is really still open to conjecture. A baby's lack of perspective at this age does not allow him to realize that he couldn't possibly fit through that tiny opening. Yet the whole idea seems a bit complex for him to think up this early. Probably the simplest means of handling the situation is to remove baby from the tub and let the water out later.

By the age of nine months, there now emerges a real possibility of a baby's becoming spoiled. This doesn't require any drastic changes in your handling of him, but you may need to be a bit more firm than in the earlier months. He needs to feel your certainty. On the other hand, baby has a difficult time coping with the many "don'ts" in his life, many of which he finds confusing and frustrating. They occasionally cause him to feel shattered, as though he has lost control of himself. His reactions may range anywhere between a hurt expression and frantic rage.

You can't help but be upset by all of this. But what baby does *not* need is either sympathy, your own reactions of fright or to be ignored. He needs calm reassurance that everything will soon be all right again. His raging is only an outlet for his frustration; it is not intended as a means of manipulating you. As long as you remain aware of that and treat it as such, your baby will gradually learn to master his feelings in a more acceptable manner.

development chart

PHYSICAL	SENSORYMOTOR	INTELLECTUAL	SOCIAL
Crawls with one hand full. Can turn around when crawling. May crawl up stairs. Sits well in chair. Gets self into sitting position effortlessly and sits alone steadily and for long times. May side-step or "cruise" along furniture. Sleep problems may be caused by practicing standing in the middle of the night.	Clasps hands or bangs objects together at center of body. Picks up and manipulates two objects, one with each hand. Drops one of two objects to get third. May build tower of two blocks. Approaches small object with finger and thumb; large object with both hands. Listens to conversations and singing tones. Feeds self cracker and holds bottle. Uses handle to manipulate and drink from cup.	Recognizes dimensions of objects. Uncovers a toy he has seen hidden. Grows bored with repetition of same stimuli. May remember game from previous day. Anticipates reward for successful completion of act or command. Can keep a series of ideas in mind. Can follow some simple instructions. Fears heights; aware of vertical space. May role-play troublesome acts; shows symbolic thinking. May say "dada" and/or "mama" as specific names.	Eager for approval. Begins to evaluate people's moods and motives. Initiates play; enjoys peek-aboo. Deliberately chooses toy for play. May be sensitive to other children; cries if they cry. May learn to protect self and possessions; may fight for a disputed toy. Imitates coughs, tongue clicks, hisses. Performs for home audience and repeats act if applauded. Wants to play near mother.

Note: These charts are to be regarded as guidelines only. Many babies will perform each activity earlier or later than indicated.

sitting

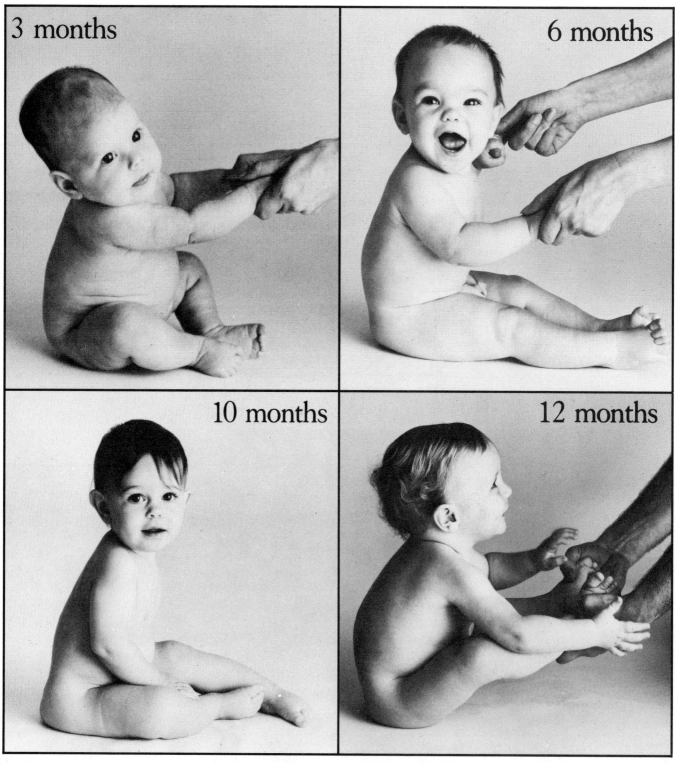

3 months

6 months

10 months

12 months

Baby is convinced that the world is his to play in, and he will dream up an infinite number of things to do.

How many times a day does the mother of a busy crawler say "no"? Perhaps it's just as well if you don't count, for surely you would conclude you must be doing something wrong. "The books " (probably including this one) imply that a properly babyproofed home should virtually eliminate the need to prevent baby from his natural pursuits.

Practically speaking, as every mother knows, it doesn't work quite that way. To begin with, there is only so much moving, unplugging, fencing off and locking up that can be done to the average home and still have it retain the semblance of a human habitat. There will always be a few off-limits areas, and baby will simply have to learn that he *may not* swing from the drapes or pull the fringe off the overstuffed chair. Although baby is now gaining a vague realization of before and after, he still lives in the world of right-now, and this creates more friction because of his demands for immediate attention.

Baby understands what "no" is all about now and may even be able to repeat the word and shake his head. This does not deter him, however. He is caught in a period of conflict: the breaking away and the holding on; the need to discover for himself and the need to please his parents. Tirelessly and noisily he rushes from one thing to another. His ears are filled with no-don't-bang-on-the-windows and no-don't-scream-like-that-when-I'm-on-the-telephone and no-don't-play-with-the-knobs-on-the-television-set.

We should mention at this point that while shaking his head is relatively easy for baby, it will be several months before he will be able to *nod* his head or say "yes."

Patience and firmness are probably beginning to sound like rather tiresome virtues at this point. Nevertheless, combined with perseverance, they are the only ways to successfully lead your baby toward eventual self-management. Any object or situation that holds potential danger for baby must be handled *very* firmly. Baby needs to understand right from the beginning that certain issues are simply *not* debatable.

Sitting, and all its related maneuvers, is now very comfortable for your baby. She can turn, lean, change position and go from prone to sitting and back again with ease. Stairs attract her almost hypnotically. Most babies keep going up and worry only after they find themselves stranded on the top. They won't be able to work their way down for at least another month yet. These are babies who require either gates across the stairs or constant supervision.

Babies of this age are in various stages of motor development. Almost all are crawling by now, and many are standing although they need help in keeping their balance. Some are cruising the furniture; a few are taking a step or two alone; and still fewer are walking. Paths of development may even differ occasionally: some babies go directly from creeping to stand-

ing, but most of them again drop to all fours to try out that all-important crawling stage.

The joy on the face of a baby who has just taught himself to walk is without equal. It is truly unfair to deprive him of that joy by trying to teach him to walk before he is ready to do it himself. While it may seem impossible to "teach" a baby to walk, it can be done. In *Infants and Mothers*, Dr. Brazelton relates an extreme example of a baby girl who was taught to walk at the age of six and a half months. When she was three weeks old, she had been placed in a jumper with her feet touching the floor, and several times each day her mother and grandmother held her by the arms and walked her. "At six and a half months," writes Dr. Brazelton, "she took stiff-legged steps forward unsupported, her arms extended rigidly, her face a mask of tension. She looked and walked like a wound-up tin soldier." At the age of three and a half years, she still walked in precisely the same manner. This is a tragic story, but it does illustrate the harm parents can generate by interfering with a baby's own pattern of development.

This does not mean you can't encourage baby, of course. Very often, for instance, that important first step alone is into the waiting arms of mother. The point is that you should know your baby well enough to understand which things he is capable of and which he is not, and do not force him to attempt the latter.

Your baby will have many falls and other minor accidents while he is learning to walk. Except in the rare case where he has really hurt himself, as long as you don't get too upset about the fall, baby probably won't either. If he does look as though he's about to burst into tears, a laugh from you—as though he has just performed a funny trick—will usually make him laugh

too. (He may even repeat the fall just to hear you laugh again.)

Parents of a quiet baby or one who is late in such skills as crawling often worry that he has so little interest in the various stages of motor development. As we've mentioned in other chapters, his interest may be on vocalizing or studying details of his playthings, and he may have no apparent concern about whether or not he can move around by himself. Usually such babies begin the various motor activities at a later date, but often it's as though they had been storing energy and mentally studying the procedures in preparation for the actual physical take-off. Once they do begin to stand or crawl or walk, learning and practice time is usually much shorter than for babies who started earlier. This phenomenon, known as "cocoon maturation," has been verified in studies of hospital-ized babies who, because of the nature of their disabilities,

could not be given the opportunity to crawl or walk at the times they normally would have done so. Upon dismissal from the hospital, the majority of these babies had caught up to their appropriate levels of development within just a few days.

As we discussed earlier, depending on what kinds of food he is now eating, constipation may occur. The problem could become more severe than earlier, however, since baby is now gaining a certain amount of sphincter control. If bowel movements are painful for him, he will tend to hold them back, thus adding to the problem. Check with your doctor. He will probably recommend prune juice, sugar or extra fluids.

Usually at about this age, baby prefers to feed himself most of his meals. He is probably switching to chopped or "junior" foods and may balk at the lumps in them. He may prefer finely chopped or soft-cooked regular foods to the so-called junior varieties, particularly if he has an older brother or sister he wants to imitate. The vegetables in commercial vegetable soup, for instance, are an ideal size and consistency, and he can pick up the pieces fairly easily with his fingers.

Sleeping patterns aren't much different than they were during the past two or three months, meaning, of course, that they vary a great deal among different babies. The excitement of new motor activities continues to interfere with sleep for many babies, and some have been known to fall asleep standing up against the crib rails. If you hear your baby awaken in the middle of the night and you peep in on him, you may find him, glassy-eyed, practicing his standing posture. In all likelihood he is barely awake, but the drive to become upright is so strong in some babies that it can carry over into their sleeping hours.

A very active baby may sleep only eleven hours at night with a one-hour nap during the day. That doesn't really seem to be enough sleep, but such babies thrive as well on this amount as others who sleep much more. Evidently this ability is due to differences in body efficiency and activity level, just as these differences caused one baby to gain more weight while eating less food than another baby.

There may be great difficulty now for your baby to make the transition from waking to sleeping. If so, he may need help for a while in learning how to relax. Try holding him in your lap, perhaps in a rocking chair, while he has his evening bottle or while you look at a picture book together. This can be a special quiet time for baby and either mother or father. The extra time required is well spent if baby is able to gradually manage a more relaxed night's sleep.

Many babies can now devise their own methods of falling asleep, even after they have wakened during the night. They find that vigorous rocking in the crib may cause it to move, and they become totally involved in developing this new method of transportation. The clatter is often horrendous as baby goes rocking, rolling and banging across the floor. (Your baby will be unhappy about it, but for your own peace of mind you may need to remove the crib wheels or block them off for a time.)

You can almost see your baby's intelligence expand. His sense of perspective is now developed enough that he can determine large and small in relation to near and far. He knows where a toy is even when he can't see it. If it's behind him, he can reach for it, without looking, from either a standing or a sitting position.

Baby can anticipate events even better now. He knows that dinner is being prepared because of the combination of sounds from the kitchen. He knows that his mother is going out when she gets her coat from the closet. A siren signals an approaching fire engine or other fast-moving vehicle with flashing lights. By learning anticipation, he is also learning how to wait for something—though not necessarily for very long or with much patience.

Vocalizing increasingly takes on the tones of a "language that isn't." Some babies this age are concentrating on motor achievements, others on language. A baby of this age may be able to say "hi," "bye-bye," or "boom" (as he hits the floor). He may also be able to imitate one or two animal sounds.

Baby's word comprehension and response gestures continue to grow. When asked, "Show me..." he can point to a fair number of objects. Don't count on a public performance, however. He usually complies only when he is in the safety of his own home and with his own family members.

Music may elicit a whole repertoire of responses. Baby may rock, sway, bounce and hum. If he's standing well, he may even attempt a back-and-forth dance step as he holds on to a support. Surprising as it may seem to the parents of a nonstop baby, quiet visual activity is very important. Studies reveal that approximately 20 percent of a baby's waking time, from now until the age of three, is spent in staring. He is especially interested in observing new kinds of stimuli: people working, machines moving and all kinds of animals. He likes to watch you as you go about various household tasks and will soon want his own set of "tools" to help you. A trip to the zoo is fascinating but probably no more so than a visit to a busy construction site.

Baby is convinced that the world is his to play in, and he will dream up an infinite number of things to do. In his travels about the house, he may carry something in his left hand (if he's right-handed), leaving his right hand free for examining and manipulating. Beware of overhanging tablecloths, especially if dinnerware is still parked on them.(It does make such a wonderful crash as it all tumbles to the floor, though.) Towels no longer remain on towel racks; they must be pulled down and preferably transported to another room. There is no toy more fascinating than the toilet: it can be swished in, waded in and is an excellent receptacle to drop things into. At least until baby is able to easily operate a doorknob, you're better off firmly declaring the bathroom off-limits by keeping the door closed.

It's a good idea to give baby his own room or part of a room in which to do whatever he wants; he won't bother the rest of the house so much. He does, after all, need a place to keep his toys, but there's little sense in expecting him to spend very much of his day there. And if there is an older brother or sister who's still in the toddler stage, keep him or her away from baby's room to avoid aggravation.

The playroom, or play area, should be equipped with shelves or open cupboards so that his toys are easily accessible. (Sturdy stacked cartons can serve as well.) Small items can be kept in baskets, plastic dishpans or similar containers. A toy chest is not especially safe or practical just yet. Even those with so-called safety catches to hold them open, have been known to slip and pinch tiny fingers.

No matter how extensive the array of baby's toys might be, if he already has his first pair of soft-soled shoes, they will become a favorite plaything. There is probably a certain amount of symbolic value attached, but baby also seems to believe that leather has a nice flavor when it's chewed. You might even see a baby dragging one shoe around by the laces or trying to wear it on his ear.

While baby enjoys exploring the world on his own, he also seeks companionship and attention. Consequently, the best way for an unfamiliar person to gain his affection is to play games with him.

Baby has now evolved his own game of peekaboo, otherwise known as "Where's the baby?" He burrows under his blanket or plunks it over his head, waiting expectantly for the question. If it isn't asked immediately, he calls out for a player. He is bright enough now to vary his reaction time, sometimes whisking the blanket away immediately, other times remaining hidden for what seems like an interminable length of time.

Another of his own versions of peekaboo is hiding his face behind his hands and assuming, ostrich-like, that if he can't see you, you can't see him either. (This is becoming a special way of saying "no" to a disliked food: he covers his eyes with his hands and just pretends he isn't there.)

Still testing his theories of disappearance and return, baby has invented the "separation" game, which means he tosses his toys into some unreachable spot and then, at a suitable moment for him, commands that they be returned. (That particular game is better suited for older siblings, who tend not to tire of it quite so quickly as parents do.)

A good way to assist baby in his still common fears of strange people and places, is to take him shopping with you frequently. Unknown places and objects seem to have a greater adverse effect at this time than people do. Various studies have revealed that a baby placed in a strange, empty room containing a number of toys not only refuses to explore but also usually just sits and cries. Even with mother present, a ten-month-old baby hesitates to examine a novelty object (although a younger baby will usually begin manipulating such an object immediately).

Your baby may already have started cooperating a bit while he is being dressed. He will probably hold up the appropriate leg when asked and help push his arms through sleeves—a far cry from the "wet noodles" you've often had to work with in the past. Water play is still very entertaining for baby. At bathtime he enjoys using a towel to dry himself, though portions of him will need some additional work.

But while baby is willing to cooperate and learn about those matters that interest him, he can exhibit the ultimate in stubbornness when it comes to learning about those that don't interest him. This is a time of many moods. Baby's drive to investigate often leads him to forbidden territory, but he cannot resist, and he thrills with the power of his latest triumph. Yet particularly when his father scolds him for his misdeed, he falls apart in disgrace. He demands more freedom yet must have his parents' approval, or the conqueror becomes the conquered.

How do babies manage to handle these conflicts? Many of them invent the security blanket. (It isn't always a blanket, per se; it may be a diaper, piece of cloth or article of clothing.) It may seem like "just another blanket" to mother, but look at it from baby's point of view: it is soft and can be molded, qualities that remind baby of his mother. Baby not only goes to sleep with his blanket but also may carry it with him for a period during the day. Many mothers are chagrined by this strong attachment, particularly after the blanket becomes overly soiled and appears to have taken up daytime residence in the middle of the living room floor. Actually, this kind of behavior is not only perfectly normal but also suggests a functioning intellect. Who but a baby could improvise such a clever device?

This attachment is to be encouraged rather than the reverse. It is baby's way of learning to cope with his world and resolve his conflicts as he strives toward independence from the one person he is most dependent on: his mother.

development chart

PHYSICAL	SENSORYMOTOR	INTELLECTUAL	SOCIAL
Stands with little support. Side-steps along furniture. Walks holding on with both hands. May be able to raise self to a standing position by straightening arms and legs and pushing up with palms. Climbs up and down from chairs and other furniture. Sits down from standing position. Turns onto stomach from sitting position. May have trouble sleeping. Helps dress self.	Sees individual objects as separate from others. Continues to learn about objects: crumples paper, rattles box, listens to watch tick. May differentiate use of hands, holding on with one, manipulating with other. Carries 2 small objects in one hand. Voluntarily releases object but does so awkwardly. Opens drawers to explore contents. Interested in fitting things together. Begins to prefer one hand and side of body to the other. Responds to music by rocking, bouncing, swaying, humming.	Reaches behind self for object he knows is there without actually seeing it. Searches for hidden object if he sees it hidden. Searches in same place for an object even though he has seen it hidden in various locations. Points to body parts on request. Increasingly imitates behaviors; rubs self with soap, feeds others. May repeat word incessantly, making it an answer to every question. Understands and obeys some words and commands.	Seeks companionship and attention. Grows aware of self and social approval, disapproval. Imitates gestures, facial expressions, sounds. Shows moods; looks hurt, sad, happy, uncomfortable, angry. Begins sexual identity; i.e., boys identify with males, girls with females. Prefers one or several toys. Enjoys water play. Displays fear of strange places.

Note: These charts are to be regarded as guidelines only. Many babies will perform each activity earlier or later than indicated.

Stooping, squatting, bending, leaning, reaching, baby continues his space and distance studies throughout the day.

More than ever, parents need to understand the conflicts of this stage of development. This is a time when baby needs your support. He needs to know that when he clambers over to you for a hug and pat of reassurance, you will cheerfully comply. If his actions strike you as "babyish," bear in mind that however much he has changed since his day of birth, he is, after all, still a baby. And don't worry if friends or neighbors think you are spoiling him.

The average age at which babies begin walking is about 12 months, while 11 months is the average age for cruising. But ranges can vary so much that you shouldn't be concerned if your baby starts a little later or earlier. If your baby has already started cruising, you'll now notice a few variations being added to his activities. Once he feels reasonably comfortable moving along a piece of furniture, he will gradually hold on more loosely, sometimes forgetting to hold on at all. He'll practice standing on one leg and on his toes. While clutching his support with one hand, he may bend over and pick a toy off the floor. After trying this a few times with one hand, he experiments with the other.

Your baby can probably pull himself to a standing position easily now and may refuse to be stood up by someone else. He lowers himself again without danger of a backward fall and halfway down may pause to bend over forward and look between his legs, intrigued by this upside-down view of his world. Stooping, squatting, bending, leaning, reaching, baby continues his space and distance studies throughout the day.

During his living room cruises, your baby may discover that he can make a fairly functional walker out of a lightweight chair. If so, this new means of locomotion will occupy a good part of his time for a while. He practices shifting his weight and taking steps as he follows along behind his new contrivance. You will need to assist him by removing any small rugs that might hinder his progress or cause him to slip.

Inevitably, however, as baby ventures those first tentative steps alone, there are bound to be at least a few falls and bumps. You will need to remain unruffled about the many minor accidents, but don't ignore them entirely. A quick hug and a few soothing words should be enough encouragement to get baby right back on his feet. If you delay your response too long, he may work himself into a real crying jag. The tears will more likely be caused by frustrations than by any real physical harm. Still unsure of his new adventuring, he needs you to tell him that he's all right and doing fine.

As soon as your baby begins walking by himself, he is ready for his first pair of shoes. Indoors, however, he should be allowed to go barefoot as much as possible to help strengthen his foot muscles. Until baby is walking very well, shoes should be soft-soled and flexible. Many mothers think their babies require the extra "support" of a hard-soled shoe. They do not, and in addition, such a shoe prevents the foot from gripping easily. Baby must walk more stiffly, which slows his development of a natural, relaxed walking gait.

From the time your baby begins walking until he is about fifteen months old, his rapidly growing feet will require a new pair of shoes every four to six weeks. After that until the age of about two years, he will need new shoes approximately every two to three months. It's difficult for budget-minded parents to discard outgrown shoes so often, particularly if they only show little wear. Yet it is imperative that baby's toes be allowed to spread naturally as he walks. Likewise, don't give in to the temptation of buying new shoes in a size too large so they'll last longer. A too-large shoe causes the foot to slip, which may either result in blisters or in baby's developing an unnatural foot position as he tries to overcompensate for the clumsiness of oversized shoes. A general rule in buying new baby shoes is one-half inch of space beyond the big toe and one-quarter inch of extra width at the widest part of the foot.

If your baby is an adventurous eleven-month-old, he may enjoy climbing and is probably attempting to get to the top of objects as high as a foot. If he has enjoyed rocking with you in the past, he may attempt to climb into the rocking chair and do his own rocking now. When he wants to climb down from the chair, he now has a pretty good idea of how far away the floor is, and he will slowly back down, using his legs as feelers. If he can't quite reach it, he'll probably stay where he is and yell for help.

Eating and sleeping patterns show little change this month. Your baby may continue to be more interested in playing and looking around than she is in eating. She tends to take a fancy to a particular food that she wants served every day (or even every meal) for perhaps two weeks at a time. It is then likely to be rejected in favor of some other food.

Some babies only take one hour-long nap at this age but will make up for it by sleeping longer at night. For some unexplainable reason most babies seem ready to take their one nap late in the morning even though they have had a long uninterrupted night's sleep. When this happens, it's often difficult for baby to make it through the entire afternoon without becoming almost intolerably cranky by dinnertime. It's probably best to encourage him to begin the habit of an after-lunch nap even if it means feeding him lunch as early as 11 a.m. for a while.

If you haven't already switched your baby's bathtime to evening rather than morning, now is a good time to do it. It will help him relax for the long night's sleep. Besides, he's usually dirtier at night from his daily travels about the house. (This is not intended as an affront to your housekeeping abilities but is merely a comment on the fact that all little people seem to be born with the ability to ferret out the dirtiest spots in which to play.)

As your baby begins to take a few steps, you may notice that his feet tend to roll inward at the edges. Known as pronated feet, this condition usually corrects itself rather quickly as baby learns to balance more easily and as his foot muscles strengthen.

Some babies, especially those who are less physically active, continue to be somewhat flop-jointed. Again, the condition will gradually disappear as baby's muscles gain more strength. A loosely jointed baby is probably not yet ready for walking since knee and hip joints don't easily remain stiff enough to support baby's weight.

You may be concerned from time to time that your baby doesn't seem to hear very well some of the things you say to him. If you have any real doubts about your baby's hearing, discuss the situation with your pediatrician. He will be able to perform simple tests to indicate whether your baby actually does require further examination of his hearing.

Ear-pulling tends to occur again, or perhaps for the first time now, as baby is beginning to cut his first molars. You can probably assume the behavior is due to teething *unless* your baby exhibits any of the following: fever, tender ear lobes, obvious pain that does not respond to baby aspirin, or white discharge from the ear due to pus, not ear wax. (Pus is distinguishable by its foul smell.) If any of the foregoing symptoms are present, there is a possibility of ear infection, and you should call your pediatrician immediately. Do not be alarmed about redness around the ear area, however. It is simply a result of the ear-tugging itself.

By now your baby has lost much of the protection against simple general infections that he had at birth. This is a classic age for his first real illness. Babies tend to respond to infections with high fevers, which can be very frightening to novice parents. In some cases the temperature may rise several degrees suddenly and go so high that baby may go into a fever convulsion; that is, he goes limp, may shake all over and may appear to stop breathing. *Do not panic.* Immediately place your baby in a tub of lukewarm water to start lowering the fever; then contact your pediatrician as soon as possible.

When fever is present, it is important to see that your baby has sufficient fluid intake to avoid becoming dehydrated. Particularly if baby's stomach is also upset, he may refuse to drink anything at all. Your doctor will probably recommend a teaspoon at a time of carbonated soft drinks (which tend to stay down more easily than other liquids), and possibly a lollipop or chunk of ice to suck on.

Baby aspirin or acetaminophen and frequent sponge baths will help keep baby's temperature from shooting up again. There is no way to avoid at least some degree of alarm the first time such an infection occurs, even though baby may be considerably older than this.

You might consider discussing the possibility of fever convulsion in more detail with your physician. That way should one occur, you're less likely to be caught off guard and forget what to do. Such extreme fever reactions don't happen to *all* babies, of course, but they do occur frequently enough that you need to be aware of how to handle the possibility.

Few babies really do much talking during their first year, and contrary to popular opinion, early talking is not a reliable sign of intelligence—or of very much else, for that matter. More important at this age is the development of baby's understanding of what is said to him. Most babies now have a passive vocabulary; that is, they know the names of about ten objects even though they can't yet pronounce them, and they are able to follow simple directions (when they wish to). This is a good time to begin adding "please" and "thank you" to your requests if you have not already been doing so. When your baby does begin talking, these simple niceties will eventually become a part of his everyday speech along with all the other words he learns to say.

Once their babies do begin talking, many parents are astonished by the speed at which the spoken vocabulary increases. At least part of the reason is fairly simple: as baby begins to talk, his parents talk more *to* him, which in turn tends to further his speaking attempts. Although we have frequently stressed the importance of talking to your baby, new parents often feel a certain amount of reluctance at continually conversing with someone who doesn't answer—at least not in the same language.

Baby talk or certain "sublanguage" terms exist in almost every language and culture of the world, and they do not seem to hinder normal speech development. Indeed such words as "bye-bye" enhance baby's initial ability to communicate since he can pronounce that simplified version long before he is able to say "good-bye." Whether or not you choose to temporarily incorporate such terms as "bow-wow" (for dog) into your baby's vocabulary, is really a personal matter. When, at about this age or a little older, you hear your baby uttering "choo-choo-choo," for example, as he pushes a toy train around the floor, it becomes obvious why he might prefer to call his train a "choo-choo." There is really no harm in this kind of usage as long as it's not overdone. You need not worry about future vocabulary confusions. Your baby will discover soon enough that many things may be called by more than one name (couch/sofa/divan/davenport, for example).

Your baby's interest in dismantling everything, particularly hinged objects, accounts in part for his increasing interest in books. But his real enjoyment extends far beyond that. What could be cozier than snuggling up to mommy or daddy or a special baby-sitter and learning of the countless marvels contained in picture books? Don't try to teach your baby any of the words or letters at this age. He isn't able to assimilate those kinds of abstractions just yet. He wants to look at the pictures and to listen to you as you read or describe them. Keep your voice lively and animated. Let him turn the pages if he wants to, and allow him to spend as much time as he wishes on each. It isn't necessary to finish the entire book at one sitting; you might often interrupt a story in the middle. The idea is for baby to form a pleasant association with books that will carry through his entire life.

Changes in your baby's play are beginning to occur now. His grasp is firmer, and he is able to use his fingers more precisely. Thumb and forefinger can now place objects more steadily, such as a key in a lock or a coin in a slot. He can hold different objects at the same time; for example, a container in one hand and items to put into it, in the other hand.

Exploratory behavior leads to the classification of toys and other objects. Baby will sort, divide and combine in many ways, often going through a series of "wrong" answers to reach what is to him, at least, the "right" solution. Stack toys are useful for this kind of activity as are a set of metal or sturdy plastic dishes, containers with lids or any object that fits into another. This is excellent preparation for the more complicated tasks of the next few months. Baby constantly studies shapes and sizes, noting the many differences between a cup and a glass, for instance. He learns that a small object fits into a larger one, but not the reverse, and that a cube must be rotated to a certain position in order to fit into another one. He becomes fascinated with the trajectory of falling objects, comparing over and over again the differences in the falling paths of heavy and lightweight objects of different shapes.

Girls as well as boys delight in all of these experiments and will go on to enjoy the more complex kinds of fitting toys in later months. If you have a girl baby, don't ever assume she is content to play only with dolls or other "girl-type" toys. Much of the difficulty traditionally encountered by girls in math classes is now attributed in large part to the fact that they were not encouraged as youngsters to play with the kinds of toys that could have helped provide an understanding of basic mathematical principles. Likewise, there is no need to discourage boy babies from playing with dolls. Along with all other types of play, it helps contribute to a well-rounded background.

Your baby also enjoys push toys of various kinds now, whether or not he has begun to walk. Even after baby is walking, push toys tend to be preferred to pull toys for the next few months. It takes most babies a while to understand what the string is for on pull toys, much less how to use it.

Baby is fascinated by sand now and still loves water. With constant supervision you *may* be able to keep the sand out of his hair, ears and mouth. Dough is also fun for him to work with. In another month or two he will probably try to form it into shapes, but right now he is content enough to poke, pat, pinch, roll it and stuff it in his mouth.

All kinds of imitative toys are of interest, such as toy dishes and household tools. By now your baby has probably accumulated quite a number of different playthings. It's wise to keep some of them put away part of the time. They can then be

rotated with others every few days to provide more novelty for baby. There will be a few special favorites, however, that he will not want to part with even for a few hours.

Baby's growing intelligence now allows him a greater grasp of what happens when a toy is hidden from view. At about this age he begins to realize that when an object is placed in a second hiding place, it is useless to return to the first hiding place to look for it. This is a considerable advance from a couple of months ago when he could only conceive of an object being hidden in one place. Try hiding a toy under several different covers at one time. As soon as baby catches on, he will have a wonderful time removing each covering until he "finds" the toy again.

Games of many kinds will usually absorb a baby for as long a time as someone is willing to play with him. Peekaboo is still in great favor, particularly now that he can participate so easily. Hide-and-seek, go-and-get games, patty-cake and similar activities are great fun.

Baby's association with her father is gaining increasing importance, perhaps because when he arrives home after work, he introduces a note of renewed exuberance. (After all, he hasn't been following baby around the house all day.) Father also symbolizes a different kind of relationship for baby. Continue to encourage baby and father to enjoy and spend time with each other.

You will notice your baby's growing awareness of the distinction between behavior that is good and that which is naughty. When he knows he has done something positive, he will often call your attention to it, either by using the word "See!" or making an equivalent sound. When he knows he has misbehaved and realizes he's about to be found out, he's likely to scramble into what he thinks is a hiding place.

A few babies may begin to throw tantrums, although this is a bit early for the full-fledged temper tantrums that occur during the second year. But it's not too soon for your baby to learn that he cannot exist in an ideal situation all of the time. Absolute security, with parents denying baby nothing, creates an unhealthy situation. It simply is not a part of the real world. Your job as parents is to help your baby eventually adjust to life as it exists, not to the kind of life that you *wish* existed.

At about this age your baby has been learning that the best way to solve a problem is to have someone else do it for him. At least part of the time, many babies will feign helplessness and expect prompt attention to their desires. Obviously, you are not doing baby a favor by always doing for him what he is able to do for himself or by failing to encourage him to attempt new tasks on his own.

Even a highly intelligent baby needs direction and an occasional push. To be born bright is not enough in itself. A baby needs other intelligent people to provide stimulation, to present problems, and when necessary, to help solve them. But as we have cautioned before, avoid becoming overinvolved in baby's activities. Don't force his attention beyond his time limit or scope of interest. Your goal is not to bore or frustrate your baby but rather to gently teach him how to think and do for himself.

development chart

PHYSICAL	SENSORYMOTOR	INTELLECTUAL	SOCIAL
Stands alone. Able to stand by straightening limbs and pushing up and off from palms while lifting body. May be able to stand by flexing knees and pushing off from squatting position. Cruises furniture; may stand on toes. May lean over while standing against support. May take a step or two without holding on. While standing, may pivot body as much as 90 degrees. Lowers self from standing position without falling. Climbs up stairs. Squats and stoops.	May use hands in sequence, i.e., in feeding; or while squatting, picking up object in one hand, holding to support with other. Picks up minutely small objects. Deliberately places objects. May carry spoon to mouth. May pull off socks and untie shoelaces. Places and removes objects into and from a cup, box or other container. Lifts lid from box. May remove and place rings on a tower cone. Turns pages of a book but not necessarily one at a time.	Aware of own actions and some of their implications. Compares same act done with each side of body. Experiments with means to attain goal; i.e., may use small chair as a walker. Associates properties with things: meows for kitten, points upward when seeing picture of a bird. Obeys commands and has established meaning of "no." Speech still gibberish with a few intelligible sounds. Can imitate inflections, speech rhythms and facial expressions more accurately than speech sounds. May say 2–3 words besides "mama" and "dada." Recognizes words as symbols for objects (i.e., when hears word "airplane," points to sky).	Imitates movements of adults and movements and play of other children. Is not always cooperative. Shows guilt at his wrongdoing. Seeks approval and tries to avoid disapproval. When praised, repeats action for additional praise. Increased dependence on mother. Reaches for mirror images of objects. Enjoys games like hide-and-seek, rolling a ball back and forth.

Note: These charts are to be regarded as guidelines only. Many babies will perform each activity earlier or later than indicated.

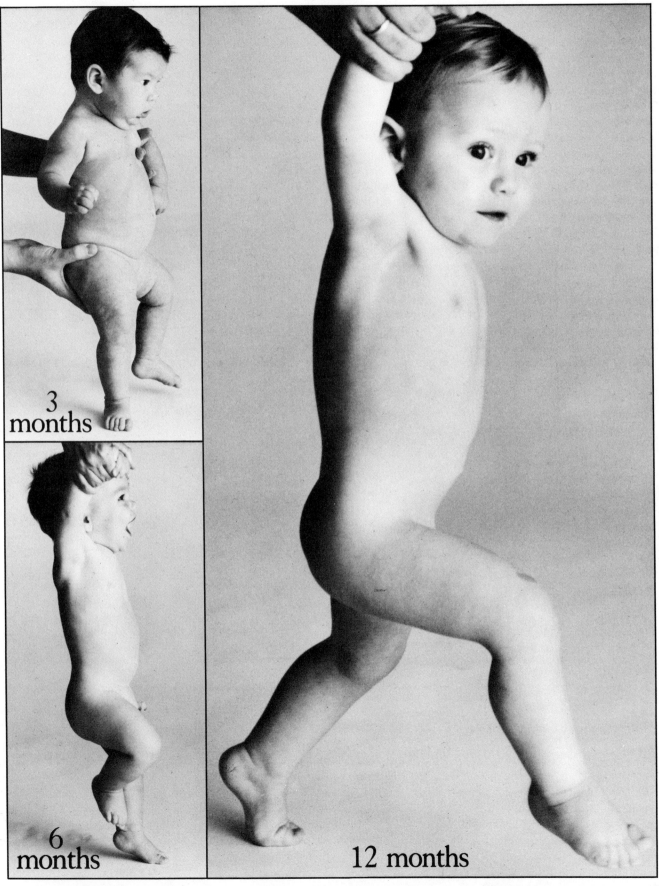

3
months

6
months

12 months

Walking is pure pleasure, but for business matters crawling gets him around more rapidly and with fewer mishaps along the way.

Observing your baby's present display of high-powered energy, it's difficult to recall the near-helpless bundle you brought home from the hospital just twelve months ago.

Your baby has a growing sense of self. He is able to perceive himself as a distinct and separate human being. He has an awareness of his size, his needs and his likes. Personality is emerging. He is becoming a person.

By the end of the month, some combination of walking, standing and cruising will absorb much of baby's time. About three out of five babies walk by their first birthday, but that date marks the *average* age when baby takes his first step. A quiet baby will stand alone by the end of twelve months even though he's not ready yet to venture into the wide-open spaces.

Once baby is standing, he wants to do little else. He probably insists on standing to be dressed, changed, bathed, and perhaps, fed. Even being forced to sit down in a stroller or car seat is viewed by him as an affront to his ego. Once he starts really walking, however, baby frequently reverts to crawling as a temporarily more efficient means of locomotion. Walking is pure pleasure, but for business matters crawling gets him around more rapidly and with fewer mishaps.

Babies vary a great deal in their methods of learning to walk. A cautious one begins by taking a tentative step or two between pieces of furniture. A more reckless baby can simply take off for the center of the room, carried forward by his own momentum until he falls. Already on the floor, he quickly scrambles on hands and knees to pull himself up again on the nearest prop, and the routine is repeated. (This kind of baby is also the one who, when climbing, tends to keep going up and up, without a care as to how he will get down again.)

You may notice your baby carrying a toy with him whenever he practices walking. The toy or other article seems to boost his confidence by providing something for him to hold on to in place of an actual support. Gradually baby learns the general mechanics of the entire walking process. As soon as he is able to walk in a straight line with reasonable certainty, he will discover how to turn corners and stop at will (without falling over). Once he is walking well, he will be able to maneuver from sitting to standing and back again without assistance. He will gradually add other bits of behavior as he walks, such as waving or "talking." A few babies will try walking backward while dragging a pull toy along behind, but push toys are usually still preferred.

A baby just learning to walk often toes in to some degree. If it is not very pronounced, your pediatrician may suggest that you temporarily reverse his shoes (right shoe on left foot and vice versa) to correct the condition until baby is walking and balancing more easily. This is a simple remedy that will not harm baby's feet when employed for a short period of time. (But, as Dr. Brazelton mentions, "Every dear old lady his mother meets on the street will remind her that she has put her baby's shoes on the wrong feet!")

By the end of the first year, your baby is probably able to sit down on a bench or chair without having to turn around and look behind him as he sits, and he can now park himself on the seat instead of sliding to the floor. An armchair is easiest for him to use, however, since he can more easily feel where he is and where he's going.

An active baby may be climbing out of his play yard and crib—to the great distress of his parents. There isn't too much you can do or should do about the play yard problem, but his crib is another matter. You have several choices there, none of which are especially attractive. Most functional is the fastening of extensions to all of the crib sides. Or you can leave one crib side down so that baby is less likely to hurt himself as he climbs in and out, but then you will need to carefully babyproof his room in case he decides to institute some of his investigative studies in the middle of the night. Other possibilities are placing a net over the top of the crib or fastening baby in with a harness. Neither of the latter is very suitable. A harness is really too restrictive for even a sleeping baby, and a net creates the impression of a cage.

A baby of this age can quite easily be taught to swim. The crawling motions come naturally to him as he exuberantly splashes around in the water. By his second or third year, he will probably develop a fear of any water that is more than a few inches deep, but right now he is oblivious to its possible danger. Obviously, you will need to remain alert and stay close to him at all times.

Mothers frequently worry about undigested food lumps that show up in their babies' bowel movements. The lumps merely indicate that baby has not completely digested all he has eaten, but even so a healthy baby absorbs enough nutrients that the food particles are nothing to worry about. Lumpy food is best for a baby of this age. He needs to become accustomed to something other than mushy foods and will soon have enough teeth to be able to chew more thoroughly. Between twelve and fourteen months, your baby will cut about six more teeth, and that is a good time to begin brushing them regularly with a small, soft toothbrush.

Your baby should be able to feed himself totally now. Too often, when a parent helps, baby senses this as pressure to eat what he doesn't want to, even though he enjoys the same food when feeding it to himself. Food idiosyncrasies become even more evident at this age in addition to a marked change in his eating habits. Baby is gaining weight at a much slower rate now, partly because his system is able to more efficiently utilize that food which he does eat. His appetite may seem abnormally small, but it probably isn't. He may eat only one really well-balanced meal a day and perhaps refuse all but a few foods. As we have mentioned before, don't force him to eat more than he wants or foods that he doesn't like. Chances are he will obtain all the nourishment he needs by choosing his own foods and deciding for himself how much of them he wants to eat.

If you are concerned that your baby is eating too little meat, your pediatrician may suggest that you increase his protein intake by regularly adding some egg to baby's meals. A few babies have developed a definite distaste for milk at this age. You can easily substitute milk puddings and similar foods.

Babies this age still need at least one good rest period a day, even though some choose not to actually sleep. While naptime is probably best taken immediately after lunch, it should conform to the rest of the day's schedule. You may wish to encourage him to nap at a different hour. Extremely active babies may sleep either more or less than other babies. One theory holds that an active baby sleeps less because he is so busy with other projects; the opposite theory suggests that an active baby becomes more tired and therefore sleeps more. There is no rule; a baby usually sleeps as much as he needs to.

By the beginning of this month, your baby will understand much of what is said to him about the activities of his everyday world. By the end of the month, he will have a speaking vocabulary of one or two words although most of them will be baby talk ("dada," "bye-bye"). His words are interspersed with continual patter in his own language, however, and may often be difficult to distinguish.

Baby is still exploring and experimenting with everything in reach. Every object must be handled, shaken, banged and moved. Next he tries rolling, spinning, pushing and dropping. Baby's study of spatial relationships continues as he tests out what happens at varying heights and distances. Action and reaction command his attention. He concentrates for many minutes on turning on and off a light switch or appliance. He is fascinated with any kind of moving object. He's becoming more adept at using a stick, ruler or similar aid to retrieve a toy that is out of reach. He delights in discovering different ways of making the same thing happen. The thinking process is functioning.

Bathtime or the kitchen sink offers still further pleasures. All floating objects are pushed underwater to find out which ones sink and which float; which bubble or squirt and which do nothing at all. A simple sponge provides endless fascination.

Mirrors have never lost their allure, but with baby's growing sense of self, he is now easily aware of the difference between himself and his mirror image. This fact is borne out by studies in which a spot of red dye was daubed on the noses of several babies, without their knowledge. When placed in front of a mirror, the babies unfailingly reached up to touch the spot on their own noses, indicating an understanding that the baby-in-the-mirror was both the same and different.

Your baby is now intrigued by many new kinds of toys and other playthings. Where before baby has been mainly interested in taking things apart, he now tries to put them back together. Plastic jars with screwtops and an old percolator are fun for him now. In imitation of adults or older siblings, he tries to manipulate objects as he sees others use them. He now uses a spoon for stirring instead of just banging and enjoys using his own collection of household gear to help clean house.

Stuffed animals are also becoming more important in your baby's life, and one or two are usually looked upon with special favor. They appear to serve either as transitional objects (from waking to sleeping) or mother substitutes. But you will notice that baby does the mothering a good part of the time, often dishing out punishment as well as love.

The researching baby now likes to empty his entire toy chest and then climb inside it himself. If he's able to close the top or if it should slip, there is a possibility of disaster. The play area should be free of slippery rugs and perhaps include whatever child-size furniture your budget permits. A small table and chair (or chairs) are worthwhile investments, but any furniture should be durable and, of course, finished with lead-free paint.

Now he is probably ready for a pounding bench and a pegboard (with *large* pegs that he can't possibly swallow). Cardboard cartons are classic playthings for children of all ages. Right now baby is probably content with simply climbing in and out, but before many more months a carton will become whatever his imagination deems it at a given moment.

When buying toys, don't take the suggested age ranges too literally. Many toys indicated for ages two to five, for instance, are often enjoyed by a much younger child even though he doesn't necessarily do the same things with them that an older child will. Conversely, some fitting toys supposedly suitable for ages one to three may be far too complicated for most one-year-olds.

One more activity that becomes a favorite of baby's about this time is one you may not appreciate too much: he delights in undressing himself and may do it repeatedly, indoors or out, throughout the day. It may be necessary to put on his clothes and sleeping garments backwards for a while until the procedure loses its novel appeal for him.

Your baby's quest for independence still vies with his needs for dependence. He may be admirably cooperative one minute, less so the next and downright negative five minutes later. He attempts to behave more amiably when there is someone nearby to play with, however. His games are becoming more sophisticated. He delights in trying to join in a word or two of singing games, such as the "Pop" in "Pop Goes the Weasel."

Baby will enjoy a playmate now, too, even though he will only play next to another baby, rather than with him. He will play more actively with an older child, however, whether brother, sister or friend. His relationship with older siblings is also not without ambivalence. While baby tends to be motivated by a brother or sister to attempt speech or game-playing, he has also encountered frequent displays of aggression from them. The older child often finds himself in a predicament over an acceptable way to retaliate. His frustrations with the young baby are frequently even stronger than are his mother's.

If you have an older child who seems to be having difficulty coping with baby, he would undoubtedly appreciate some extra attention from you, particularly now that baby doesn't need you quite so much of the time. Try giving the older one a minimum of half an hour a day of your undivided attention, perhaps while baby is napping or after he has been put to bed for the night. It will do wonders for the child's self-esteem and will generate greater patience in his attitude toward baby.

If, on the other hand, this baby is your first and you now have a second on the way, don't be too surprised at baby's sudden demands for extra attention. Because of the extremely close association that has existed between mother and baby, he can sense a difference even though he has no real idea of what it is.

Most babies continue to need their mothers nearby during part of the day. In a strange place mother must stay close, but there are great differences in how much of the time baby wants her near him at home. Few, if any, other persons will ever elicit this kind of attachment from him. Stranger anxiety follows a similar pattern; that is, it is far less pronounced when baby is in his own home than when he is in other people's homes. Even though it may seem as though he has partially overcome these fears during the past two or three months, there is a tendency for them to reappear now.

Studies with twins indicate that a baby's predisposition toward shyness or sociability tends to be partly inherited. There is also evidence that attitudes may be picked up from the mother but not necessarily in direct correlation: a mother who is overly shy and a mother who is extremely extroverted may each unwittingly influence their babies toward shyness.

By the end of this month your baby will show his expanding sense of humor. When you laugh at something he has done, he warms to your laughter and tends to repeat the act over and over. Similarly, he appreciates the things you do that are funny to him. When his demands become overwhelming, rather than responding with anger, you might try reacting with a funny face and behaving as though his outrageous wishes are nothing short of ridiculous. A touch of humor may not change his mind, but at least it tends to make his thwarted desires a bit easier to swallow.

Baby is becoming more aware of good and bad, and he is just beginning the formation of a rudimentary conscience. Unfortunately, none of this prevents occasional lapses into temper tantrums. If this happens with your baby, don't lose your own temper just because baby has. You are the one who must remain in control, and that is really what your baby expects from you. You can either walk calmly away from him or put him in his own room and close the door. It's surprising how much the duration of a tantrum is shortened by the simple fact that there is no audience to play to.

Give him what assistance he requires for those tasks that he cannot yet handle, but don't become his "tool" by doing everything for him just because it's easier—either for you or for him. A good foundation established now will set a pattern for many years to come as your youngster reaches toward responsibility, maturity and greater independence.

Too frequent displays of anger only become ineffective, however. If you are constantly after baby for one thing or another, he will eventually pay little attention to correction from you. Save your more forceful remonstrance for the two areas of greatest importance: behavior that is potentially dangerous and behavior that interferes with the rights of others.

We are not, of course, speaking of severe physical punishment. No child, of whatever age, should be treated in such a manner; a baby doesn't even understand it. A light slap or spank, if necessary, and a firm tone of voice are sufficient. Follow a simple, firm "No!" with a substitute action or object. By suggestion, distraction and humor, you will usually be able to make baby think he's doing what he wants to anyway.

We have stressed before the need for consistency in disciplining your baby. As he grows older, however, he discovers there are times when consistency is not always possible. For instance, in the morning it may be all right for him to pull all the pots and pans out of the cupboard to play with in the middle of the floor. But late in the day when you are preparing dinner for expected company, you will probably want your kitchen equipment kept where it belongs. This is confusing to a younger baby, but your one-year-old will begin to understand your explanations. While he needs the security of as much consistency as possible, he must realize it simply cannot occur *all* of the time. Life, after all, is inconsistent, and baby can begin to learn to cope with these inconsistencies at home. He will gradually perceive that he, too, is not always consistent in his needs, desires and behavior patterns.

Baby's first birthday marks the end of babyhood. This by no means implies that it is also the end of babyhood behavior, but the helplessness of infancy has been left far behind. Baby is now well on the path toward maturity. He is learning to think, to do, to set limits on his behavior, to get along with others and with himself. The unique baby is on his way to becoming a unique child.

development chart

PHYSICAL	SENSORYMOTOR	INTELLECTUAL	SOCIAL
Displays some combination of standing, walking and cruising.	Reaches accurately for something as he looks away.	Perceives objects as detached and separate, to be imitated and inserted into play routines.	Expresses many emotions and recognizes them in others.
When standing, pivots body 90 degrees.	Uses and reaches with a preferred hand.	Unwraps toys; finds toy hidden under box, cup or pillow.	Gives affection to humans and favored objects like toys and clothes.
If walking, probably still prefers crawling as more efficient way of getting around.	Puts things back together instead of just taking apart.	Searches for hidden object even if he hasn't seen it hidden but only remembers where it was last seen.	Shows greater interest in what adults do.
May add other maneuvers to walking: stopping, waving, backing, carrying toys.	Builds a tower of 2–3 blocks after watching demonstration.	Remembers events for longer period.	May demand more help than necessary from adult because it's easier.
Gets self to standing position by flexing knees, pushing off from squatting position.	Likely to put 1–2 objects in mouth or under arm, grasp a third.	Can group a few objects by shape and color.	May refuse to eat new foods or to be fed by mother.
Climbs up and down stairs.	Uses pegboard and hammer board.	Identifies animals in picture books or magazines.	Resists napping; may have tantrums.
May climb out of crib or play yard.	Cares for doll or teddy bear by feeding, cuddling, bathing.	Responds to directions and understands much of what is said to him about his everyday world.	Fears strange people and places.
Lowers self to sitting position with ease.	Enjoys water play in bath or sink.	Experiments with spatial relationships: heights, distances.	Reacts sharply to separation from mother; needs to be near her in strange places.
Makes swimming movements in bathtub.		Experiments with action and reaction.	Distinguishes self as more definitely separate from others.
May have trouble sleeping; usually takes only one nap.		Beginning to develop conscience.	
Probably insists on self-feeding.		Babbles in short sentences.	
May undress self.			

Note: These charts are to be regarded as guidelines only. Many babies will perform each activity earlier or later than indicated.

THE LEARNING EXPERIENCE

How to be a better teacher to your child
by Dr. Burton L. White

INTRODUCTION

T hough no one knows for sure, many of us who are professionally concerned with babies believe that parents are the most important teachers a child will ever have.

Research on the development of babies has increased dramatically since 1965, and we now have a much clearer and more detailed picture of how a child develops in the first years of life. We have also learned much about what goes on in the baby's environment, specifically the home—an area which, until recently, had been largely ignored. We have completed the most extensive study ever done of children who, by their third birthdays, had achieved outstanding success in intellectual and language development while retaining delightful, unspoiled personalities.

It is from this new research, especially the studies of the Harvard University Preschool Project, that the following suggestions were developed. They are intended to help you achieve the very best possible results and have the most pleasure in the process. We are confident that if you use these ideas and the information found in the first part of this book, you, too, will be successful at child raising and will have heightened enjoyment in raising your baby. We are also confident that you will be able to avoid needless anxiety and stress (although some is inevitable when raising young

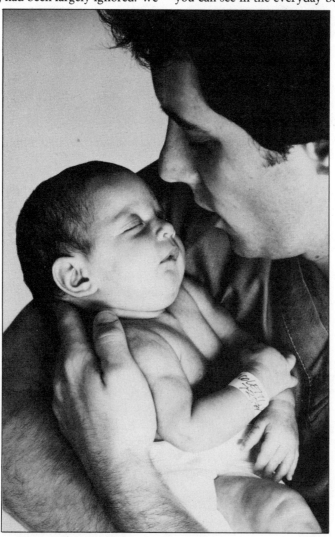

children). Furthermore, we believe that your influence on the development of your baby's abilities and personality will be stronger and more beneficial.

GOALS

What do we mean when we say we want our children to get a good start in life? The following is what we have learned from research about the behavior of outstanding and well-developed three-year-olds. Here are the abilities you can see in the everyday behavior of such children.

Intellectual Abilities

Abstract thinking ability—being able to manipulate ideas and use them to solve problems.

Observational skills—being able to notice small differences when things or events are not quite right.

Anticipating consequences—being able to think ahead to what would happen "if."

Making interesting associations—being able to use imagination to produce interesting ideas.

Planning and carrying out complicated activities—being able to organize a series of actions.

Using resources effectively—being able to improvise when necessary.

Taking another's point of view—being able to see things as they appear to another person.

Dual focusing—being able to concentrate on a task in a busy atmosphere and at the same time keep track of surrounding events.

Social Abilities

Being able to get and hold the attention of adults in a variety of socially accepted ways.

Being able to express affection or mild annoyance to adults and peers when appropriate.

Being able to use adults as resources after determining that a task is too difficult to handle alone.

Being able to show pride in achievement.

Being able to engage in role play or make-believe activities.

Being able to lead and follow children of the same age.

Being able to compete with agemates.

If a three-year-old has acquired this pattern of abilities, we believe she has had a "superior education" during her first years. Furthermore, such a foundation probably goes a long way toward ensuring that a child will enter school well-prepared for future development.

HOW TO GET STARTED

In order to do a really good job as a baby's first teacher, some information is necessary. Perhaps the best starting point is the fact that babies change at a very rapid rate during the first year of life. Actually, you'll be teaching many different kinds of children during this short time. In contrast to adults or even older children, a baby's educational needs shift repeatedly during this early period. For example, a toy for a two-year-old won't make any sense for a six-month-old. It's as if you were teaching in a public school and in September you were teaching seven-year-olds; in November the seven-year-olds left and you were dealing with twelve-year-olds; in February the twelve-year-olds left and you were facing sixteen-year-olds. Presenting the same material throughout the year wouldn't make much sense.

In order to learn more about babies, it helps to see the first three years of life in seven different periods or phases. Our ideas about parents as teachers will be presented by these phases, and we will concentrate on what is generally true about all babies for each phase. You, of course, will have to use this information as a framework for understanding rather than as a precise description of your child. A brief reminder: while each baby is unique, all babies are similar in fundamental ways.

Using this brief description of the seven phases of the first three years as a guide will help you in your role as your child's first teacher. While recognizing that your child will develop her own individuality as she grows, your understanding of her rapidly shifting interests, abilities, and needs will increase the likelihood of better results.

Dr. Burton L. White is currently the head of the Center for Parent Education in Newton, Massachusetts. For over 20 years he has specialized in the study of the development of babies and with the help of a large staff and funds from the government and private foundations, has conducted unique research by studying babies in their homes. These homes included a wide variety of income and educational levels and numerous ethnic backgrounds. His book The First Three Years of Life *(Avon, $4.95) is published in several countries.*

SEVEN PHASES OF DEVELOPMENT DURING THE FIRST THREE YEARS OF LIFE

Phase I—birth to 6 weeks

This is a transition period between pre- and postnatal life. The baby will show very limited interest in learning during this phase.

Phase II—6 weeks to 3½ months

Interest in looking increases dramatically during this period. Looking at other people's eyes and at their own hands are clear signs that a baby's curiosity has begun to control much of his behavior. Also, from this point on, babies stay awake for much longer periods during the day.

Phase III—3½ to 5 months

The key to this phase is the hands. One of the major achievements of the early months is mastery of the hands as tools. Along with continued interest in people's faces, hand-eye activity is very important at this time. Another new interest of major importance, interest in *sounds,* occurs during this period.

Phase IV—5 to 8 months

This is the quiet period of infancy. Not yet able to crawl, most babies focus on hand-eye activities, simple socializing, listening to and experimenting with sounds, and practicing motor activities like turning over and sitting up.

Phase V—8 to 14 months

Learning leaps forward at an impressive pace during this period. Language learning, mastering the body, satisfying curiosity, and getting to know the person around whom the day revolves, are all vital and very active processes of this period. (This is also the time when sibling rivalry often begins in a major way.)

Phase VI—14 to 24 months

Few periods in childhood are as fascinating as this one. Personality development is probably the most dramatic theme, and toddlers are trying out their newfound sense of power as individuals. This is also, however, a time of rapid language growth; speech appears and grows steadily. Both processes help the child to work through the attachment process with at least one grownup in her life.

Phase VII—24 to 36 months

The third year is a rich developmental period. Attachment is now a settled issue, and the child moves ahead rapidly in language, intelligence, and imagination. Now all the basic learning of the first two years is beginning to come together in productive ways. The child can now create pictures, scenes, and stories. He can express a series of ideas to another person, and interest in play with other children of the same age begins to grow.

THE CORNERSTONE OF OPTIMAL DEVELOPMENT
Phase I – birth to 6 weeks

What can you teach a brand-new baby? The answer to that question depends on the baby's ability to learn and her developmental needs. Reading stories to newborns doesn't seem to teach them anything at all about words or ideas. Indeed it hardly seems appropriate for this age. What about practice in mastering the body? You could move the baby's arms and legs through exercise routines, but there is no evidence that this serves any purpose. What about helping develop the child's mind?

The most accurate picture of the growth of intelligence in babies comes from the work of the late Swiss child psychologist, researcher, and author Jean Piaget. In Piaget's view newborns have no mental abilities of consequence. Hard as it might be to accept, behind those baby blue eyes, not much is happening. New babies come equipped with a few simple and very useful skills, such as sucking, swallowing, sneezing, and even the ability to glance at people and things, but these activities take place without the baby's thinking about them or "deciding" to do them. In the same sense that adults don't "plan" to sneeze or blink their eyes, new babies don't "plan" *any of their actions at all.* What does a teacher do with such a student? She turns to what *can be done* for a baby.

The single most important contribution an adult can make to a new child begins in the first weeks of life. On this point at least, all modern students of early development agree: during the first weeks of life, a baby needs comforting when he's distressed. This common-sense notion is of vital importance.

The classic question new parents ask about the inevitable crying of newborns is, "Shall I let him cry it out, or should I try to comfort him?" The answer is, respond promptly to a new baby's crying as often as you can. It is important to know, however, that very few parents are consistently successful at comforting their babies. If, after you've exhausted all methods including cuddling, rocking, feeding, and diapering, your baby continues to cry, you will have to let her "cry it out." The main point is that letting a baby "cry it

out" should be a last resort only, *not a routine policy.*

Frequent discomfort is inevitable during a baby's first weeks. No matter how healthy the baby or how attentive his parents, it will happen. This difficult situation serves a useful purpose, however. Newborns are not great students, but they do "learn"—not by thinking about problems but through conditioning. Each time a crying, uncomfortable baby is made to feel better by being picked up, held closely, rocked, fed, or comforted by whatever means a parent uses, the baby *unconsciously* begins to "learn" to associate the grownup's arrival with "feeling better." Little by little over the first months of life the grownup's face, voice, and even her smell and characteristic way of holding a baby come to mean relief from distress. How does a baby spell relief? M-O-T-H-E-R is usually the answer. (F-A-T-H-E-R can serve this function too.) Such experiences, especially frequent during the first weeks of life, constitute one of the two major ways in which babies acquire the foundation for healthy, lifelong interpersonal relationships. *Nothing you could do for a child is more fundamental or important.*

A Baby's First Toy

It's almost a tradition to buy rattles for babies as a first gift. Unfortunately, new babies are totally uninterested in rattles. In fact, they are hard to interest in any toy during the first weeks of life. By three or four weeks, however, they are ready for their first toy, but it's still not a rattle; it's a mobile. The baby's first signs of interest in exploring the world have to do with "looking" behavior, especially looking at faces and hands. While this interest is very strong in Phase II (6 weeks to 3½ months), like most early activities, it is likely to begin a bit earlier.

Between three and six weeks of age, babies spend most of their time in cribs and bassinets. An infant seat, which will become quite useful when they get to be between three and six months of age, isn't advisable at this early stage because babies younger than this have poor head control and weak back muscles. However, you can use the infant

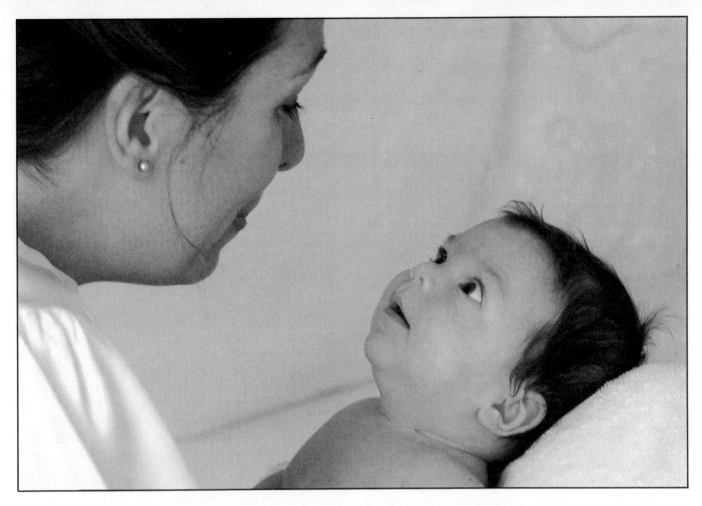

seat at a slant if you are especially careful that the low back angle provides the necessary head support.

A properly designed mobile can be something interesting for the baby to look at during his first periods of alertness. Though there are many types of mobiles available, few meet the baby's needs. Rather, they are designed to look attractive to an adult entering the baby's room.

How to Use a Mobile

1) A mobile for "looking" is best for the baby who is between three to about nine weeks of age.

2) About four out of five babies this age look to their right most of the time, so the mobile is best positioned to the baby's right side. At times they will shift their head position and turn to their far left. If your baby tends to favor her left side, place her mobile off to her left. Babies will rarely look directly overhead during this time of life, so placing a mobile directly over the midline of such a baby doesn't make much sense. But a mobile on the right side and another on the left is a good idea.

3) Three- to nine-week-old babies don't focus well on objects that are closer than eight or nine inches or farther away than about 16 to 18 inches. A mobile is best positioned between about ten to 13 inches from the baby's eyes.

4) Babies this age like to look at faces, particularly the eyes and nose, so the design of the mobile should reflect this preference.

5) Three- to nine-week-old babies do not appreciate fine detail or subtle colors. They respond best to bold colors and areas of high contrast such as human eyes and hairlines.

6) Support the mobile (bending its wire stand about 30°) so that what the baby looks at is positioned to her right.

7) As an alternative you might suspend the mobile from the ceiling using masking tape and string. Since the baby won't be pulling at it, the support need not be very strong. The thing to remember is where the mobile should be placed. Some parents have also discovered that using a mobile over the changing table helps make diapering easier.

Use of a mobile with Phase I babies (birth to 6 weeks) is not really of vital importance for a baby's development. Rather, it should be considered as the first step in a lengthy process of designing the world around a baby so that parts of it make sense in light of her rapidly changing abilities.

During this period babies begin to show a great deal of interest in their own hands. At first, this interest takes two forms—sucking and looking. The six-week-old is not, however, very good at sucking his hand. While some such babies can even suck their thumbs or fingers (thereby at times soothing themselves), most suck away at their fists and then only clumsily.

It is in the innumerable activities involving their hands, eyes, mouth, and objects they touch that babies move from helplessness to a partial understanding and control of their world. This hand-eye activity of the first years of life is one of the foundations of intellectual ability, but in order for it to grow best, the baby has to feel secure and loved. And that's a job that most parents can do well.

Another factor to keep in mind is the baby's curiosity. All healthy babies begin to show a deep curiosity about "what's out there" during the first month of life.

THE WORLD OUTSIDE
Phase II – 6 weeks to 3⅓ months

During the 1940s Arnold Gesell was perhaps the leading authority on practical information about babies. One important observation of his remains true today: toward the end of the second month of life, babies rather abruptly become much more alert and interested in looking at the world around them.

While your six-week-old will probably sleep most of the day, your ten-to-twelve-week-old will be awake for longer periods (approximately one-third of the day). During those increasingly long periods of alertness, he'll show more interest in looking at his surroundings. He'll become more curious about looking at your face, especially your eyes.

Although his hand is often in his line of sight, he is not likely to look at it directly early in Phase II (6 weeks to 3½ months). Some time between eight and twelve weeks of age, you will find that he has begun to stare at his hand. This event indicates that his visual abilities have grown to the point where he is now comfortable looking at small, nearby objects.

Once your baby starts to look steadily at his own hands, he enters into a new stage with respect to his interests and his development. From that time on he will no longer be content with just looking at what's out there. He'll now be interested in touching as well as looking.

This desire to touch is part of the process that will lead to the ability to reach by the time he is about five months old. In the beginning, however, touching consists mostly of striking or batting objects with a fist. It is not until some time during the third month of life that babies are able to use their fingers effectively for exploration. Fisted hands, the common condition of babies less than ten weeks old, restricts hand activity until that time. Nevertheless, objects within striking distance should be provided.

The central fact to remember is that a baby who has become a hand-watcher will enjoy banging objects and gradually (as he gets a bit older) exploring their shapes with his fingers. Note that

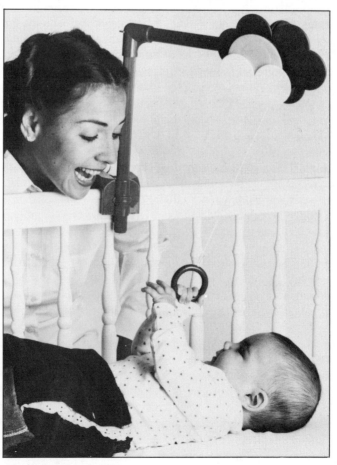

objects suspended by string are less appropriate for this stage than those that yield slightly when struck, then return to place. String-mounted objects can be frustrating to an infant who is just beginning to learn to reach.

During Phase II (6 weeks to 3½ months) prior to the emergence of hand-watching, your baby will continue to show interest in the mobile you provided in Phase I (birth to 6 weeks). In addition to crib toys suitable for hand-eye activity, older Phase II babies enjoy looking in a mirror. Find a good quality, *unbreakable* mirror or mirror toy at least six inches in diameter, and place it just out of the baby's reach (seven to eight inches away). It can be placed overhead but will be looked at more often if placed on her far right side.

With well-designed mobiles and crib toys and a well-placed mirror, you're guaranteed a Phase II baby with interesting things to do. Such a child will not only practice new skills but will also begin to satisfy and probably expand her curiosity provided one other psychological area of her life is taken care of. That area is the social-emotional area referred to earlier as the "cornerstone" of optimal development. It becomes easier now for you to meet the baby's basic need to be comforted during Phase II (6 weeks to 3½ months) for several reasons. First of all, the normal anxiety about having a baby has by this time subsided, at least somewhat. Next, by the end of the second month, most babies begin to sleep through the night and do better at taking in and digesting milk. Third, by the end of the second month, babies begin to smile regularly and to look even more attractive.

One other important pointer concerns talking to your baby. Even though babies can't understand the meaning of words until they are six to eight months old, it is very important that you begin talking to your baby much sooner. Get into the habit of talking whenever you are with him. The more the better. Also get into the habit of talking *about what your baby is attending to at the moment;* this is when he will learn best.

74

YOU'D BE SO EASY TO LOVE
Phase III – 3½ to 5 months

I have often remarked about how lovable a four-month-old baby is and how easy it is to care for such a child. There's a very special quality of serenity about the baby. By now she is an established member of the family. The thought that you could never succeed at being a parent is now obsolete. Above all, there is the baby's smile and chronically good mood. Of course, there are exceptions—all babies get cranky at times, and some will occasionally seem uncomfortable and unhappy throughout the first half year of life. Most babies, however, seem contented and highly sociable between the fourth and sixth months.

Because babies cannot survive without help, they have to form a strong attachment to some adult. The other side of this coin is that some adult has to fall totally in love with the baby. Babies are well-equipped to encourage this latter need. At first, it is their helplessness combined with their ability to produce piercing cries for lengthy periods of time that leads to nurturance. But it is doubtful if such circumstances, painful as they can be, would work month after month. The first smile arrives in the nick of time, and as if to make sure that the attachment will be complete, the four-month-old looks and acts in such a way that he is irresistible to grownups.

A baby's head takes a fair amount of pressure during the typical birth process, and as a result, many babies don't really look their best during their first months. By the middle of the fourth month, however, any unsightliness caused by the birth process has usually disappeared, and there's even some hair to help the baby look better. Added to the improved physical appearance is the remarkable increased sociability and the emergence of delight and giggling, so the probability of some grownup's making a total commitment to the baby is very high. And well it ought to be because in a matter of a few months, the job of child-rearing will become more difficult and quite a bit more stressful.

As the Phase III (3½ to 5 months) baby's first teacher, your first chore, then, is to succumb to his charms. You must not stand in the way of your natural inclination to adore that child. If you're like most "lovers," you'll not only be very affectionate with the baby, but also you will direct quite a few words his way. Great.

The more you talk to a baby, the better. Furthermore, the more you gush or show enthusiasm, the better. Excitement is contagious. If a parent shows excitement and warmth to an infant, the infant will respond in kind. What could be better?

If your Phase III child receives abundant affection, attention, and enthusiasm, is that enough to ensure his optimum progress in all ways? I don't think so. There is much to be done in the areas of hand-eye skill and satisfaction of curiosity.

By about four months of age, most babies have acquired mature visual abilities. They are usually able to track objects that move toward or away from them with impressive accuracy. They can also follow moving targets in all other directions. Their eyes turn smoothly toward approaching objects, and as a result, they can appreciate three-dimensionality or the depth of objects. With a few minor exceptions, their ability to use their eyes is just about fully developed as is the development of hearing.

Mature visual abilities are necessary if a child is to acquire a key visual-motor skill: reaching. It is through the use of the hand as a tool that much early exploration proceeds. It is largely through hand-eye activities that babies enter into the world of problem solving and the exploration of small objects. Perhaps the most obvious learning challenge of Phase III (3½ to 5 months) is the mastery of the hands as tools.

If you pay no attention whatsoever to a child's hand-eye behavior, she will nevertheless learn to reach before she is six months old. Like most of the absolutely basic skills of babies, development will take place without much help from adults, as long as adults don't actually *prevent* development. A baby without crib toys still has things to learn to reach with—the crib rails, the sheets, her own clothing, and perhaps most interesting of all, her own hands. In fact, most babies in Phase III spend lots of time with their hands clasped to each other!

Yet the key to a baby's interests is whatever process or skill is emerging at the time. For the Phase III baby (3½ to 5 months) one of the most important emergents is the ability to use the hand as a tool. Therefore, if you want to help such a baby

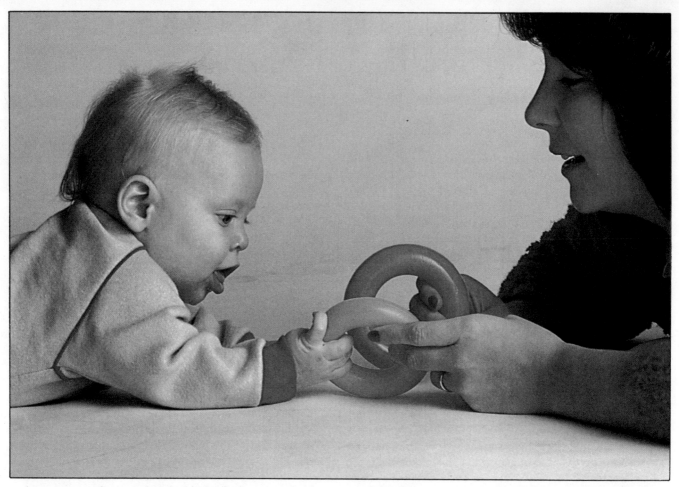

learn, you ought to get her the kinds of crib toys and objects that can be placed overhead in such a way that they help her learn to reach.

Toys For Reaching

You can find a crib toy that can be suspended over the supine baby (flat on her back) so that small, attractive, and safe objects are within reach of the baby's hand.

Don't suspend the objects by strings, and they shouldn't be objects that swing freely when hit. The ideal arrangement is a semi-rigid mounting so that the object yields when struck or pushed but returns to place when untouched. If a soft noise can be produced when the object is struck, the results will be better, but sound is not required.

You can identify true visually-directed reaching by offering a small object (larger than 1½ inches for safety's sake) to a baby about five inches away from her eyes and off to her favored side. If she brings her hand directly to the object and either begins to open or close it *just before* contact and grasp, she has acquired the skill. Earlier responses include banging the object with a fist or bringing both hands toward the object and clasping them together or batting the object with a fist and then fumbling to grasp it.

Once a baby has learned to reach, his interest will shift to using his hands for exploring objects, releasing them, and making things happen. But without special materials or assistance, the four-month-old won't be able to engage in much activity of this sort for a while. If, for example, you offer him a rattle, he will reach for and take it. He will then bring it closer for inspection with his eyes, mouth, and other hand. When he drops it, however, and he soon will, he won't be able to retrieve it or even show that he misses it.

Suitable hand-eye play for such a baby involves several differently shaped, safe objects for handling and the opportunity to create simple effects by hand-eye action. Placing the child on a blanket that has several toys within reach (and being prepared to retrieve them regularly) will involve the baby for a while several times a day.

Phase III babies (3½ to 5 months) continue to enjoy mirrors. They will also appreciate a resistant surface to kick against. The reason for this latter interest is that their leg muscles are growing stronger in preparation for that time a few months from now when they will have to support the weight of their body.

Experimenting with sounds is an activity that will lead to a later achievement. Phase III babies (3½ to 5 months) make wonderful small noises. Now that hearing has become more acute, they begin to be interested in variations in sounds, especially their own. If you quietly approach the baby early in the morning, you may hear her playing with her own saliva sounds. Though she has developed to the point where she doesn't startle as readily to loud noises as she did in earlier phases, she is still sensitive to such sounds, so you might keep voices and other sources of nearby sounds soft.

If the Phase III baby (3½ to 5 months) receives lots of attention from her parents; hears a good deal of language from them; senses that they are enthusiastic about her; is given the opportunity to engage in a good deal of hand-eye behavior; and is encouraged in large muscle practice such as leg thrusts against resistance, and turning over, she'll arrive at the next phase in great shape.

THE LULL BEFORE THE STORM
Phase IV-5 to 8 months

Phase IV is perhaps the most uneventful period of the first three years, and it's just as well because toward the end of the period, most (but not all) babies begin to get around on their own. Most begin to crawl, some scoot, some drag themselves along, some even use rolling over to get from here to there. Some powerful force must be at work! And it is. It's a combination of curiosity and the need to gain complete control over the body. You can think of infancy as a time when within each healthy child, there is a need to explore the world (at least the home), but that need is restricted by the infant's limited capacity to control his own body. As the months go by, those limitations are shed, and each time they are, the urge to explore can be satisfied more fully and in more diverse ways.

The Phase IV infant (5 to 8 months) wants very much to explore, but until he acquires the ability to move about, he's really stuck. To make matters worse, he spends lots of time looking around the room he's in, and with his fully developed vision and hearing, he can now see and be enticed by innumerable temptations, all beyond his reach. What frustration!

You might consider a walker for such a baby. What with his new capacity to be comfortable in the vertical orientation and his powerful leg extension reflex, he can actually maneuver a well-made walker before he can crawl. Infants in walkers can enjoy themselves tremendously, but they can also reach dangerous objects (including electric cords), and they can get their fingers caught in such places as door jambs, so be sure your child *is carefully supervised.*

From seven to eight months on, parents should employ discipline in the form of clear and consistent limit-setting policies. If such actions are begun as soon as the child begins to crawl, they are usually effective. Furthermore, both parents and children become accustomed to basic ground rules. The child will not feel less loved when she learns from her very first excursions around the home that she can't always go when and where the spirit moves her. When the trip is to part of the floor where you're sweeping up broken glass, or to the top of the stairs where you've forgotten to close a gate, you'll not think twice about the issue of control. You should be just as forthright when the trip is likely to destroy part of an unread newspaper. Though the child may not be in danger in the latter case, the important point is that by allowing her to ruin the newspaper, you will have begun to draw the line between her rights and yours slightly more into your territory than you should. Many a child learns from experiences of his first years that no one else in the world is quite as important as he is. In an eight-month-old this matters little; in a three- or even two-year-old, it will matter a great deal.

What else can you do to help a Phase IV baby (5 to 8 months) move ahead? Not much, directly, but you can encourage the baby's interest in the use of his hands in the manner described for the precocious Phase III baby (3½ to 5 months). Exploration of small, safe objects is fascinating to the baby. Ideas about the world of objects grow during this period so that gradually the baby's focus will begin to shift from the act of releasing or dropping the object to the motion of the object as it falls. He drops it and looks at the consequences.

Partly because of the onset of teething and partly because the mouth is still a primary tool for exploration, babies enjoy gumming objects at this stage.

Toys can now be used to give him practice in making things happen. Bath toys that encourage the baby to explore the infinite variability of water become appropriate once he can sit well (not much before seven months, however). Toys that can be operated with the light push of a button or lever can also be used toward the end of this phase. The effect has to be dramatic to hold his attention.

The two most important jobs for parents now are assuring that the baby hears well and redesigning the home.

Detecting Hearing Loss Early

Few parental activities are more important in raising a baby than regular testing for hearing losses. The Phase IV (5 to 8 months) baby is about to enter a crucial learning period, eight months to three years. Should he fail to hear well for long periods of time, he will fail to learn language as well as he might. To the extent that language learning is negatively affected during the first years, so, too, is the development of higher mental abilities affected. To the extent that both processes suffer, the child will also be hindered in respect to social development.

While babies with profound hearing loss are usually identified very early in life, those with mild to moderate losses are often not identified until they enter school. Parents can be on guard for warning signs throughout the child's early years. The following chart, prepared with the help of the Alexander Graham Bell Association for the Deaf, is offered as an aid for monitoring your child's progress. Most leading authorites agree that the procedures in the chart are useful in detecting hearing loss.

At Age	Danger Signals
Birth–3 mos.	Baby is not startled by sharp clap within three to six feet; is not soothed by mother's voice.
3–6 mos.	Doesn't search for source of sound by turning eyes and head; doesn't respond to mother's voice; doesn't imitate own noises, such as ooh, ba-bas, etc; doesn't enjoy sound-making toys.
6–10 mos.	Does not respond to own name or to telephone ringing or to someone's voice when not loud; is unable to understand words such as "no" and "bye-bye."
10–15 mos.	Cannot point to or look at familiar objects or people when asked to do so; cannot imitate simple words and sounds.
15–18 mos.	Is unable to follow simple spoken directions, and does not seem able to expand understanding of words.
Any age	Does not awaken or is not disturbed by loud sounds; does not respond when called; pays no attention to ordinary crib noises; uses gestures almost exclusively to establish needs rather than verbalizing or watches parents' faces intently.

If you suspect that your Phase IV infant (5 to 8 months) doesn't hear everything she should, insist on an examination by a pediatric audiologist, if possible. If not, write to:

The Alexander Graham Bell Society
3417 Volta Place, N.W.
Washington, D.C. 20007

for information on the nearest appropriate resource, and use it! Whenever a sign of loss is detected, careful diagnosis and follow-up are imperative.

Safety First

The second vital task for parents now is redesigning the home. There are two parts to the job; making the home safe *for* a newly crawling child and protecting the home *from* the newly crawling child. One of my key recommendations for

Phases V through VII (8 to 36 months) is to provide interesting experiences for the child. The easiest way to initiate the process is to give the child extensive access to the home. Crawling babies love to move from room to room. In the process they find an infinite number of new objects, situations, and challenges for their motor abilities. But homes are designed for adults, not babies. They are dangerous for babies. Accidental poisonings are common during infancy once the baby can crawl. All potentially dangerous materials—especially cleaning substances—must be out of reach or locked up. Electric cords and fixtures must be safe and out of reach. It's a good idea to get safety plugs for outlets. Plants must be moved out of reach. Knives and other sharp utensils must also be stored in safe places. Floors must be examined closely for small items such as forgotten pieces of broken china or ash trays. If you have stairs, a gate on the third step is advisable to allow for safe climbing with minimal supervision.

As for protecting the home *from* the baby, remember that anything breakable is fair game for an infant. If you treasure it, put it away.

If you don't redesign your home, the newly crawling baby will be a regular source of stress for you. Many parents don't do enough in this regard and then find that they're working too much at control. An occasional prohibition is more likely to work with this child than a chronic one—and it's much less work. All this is not as time-consuming as it appears. Furthermore, the redesign is a temporary affair. Once the baby reaches her second birthday, much of the home can be returned to its former state.

For most of Phase IV (5 to 8 months), your baby is likely to be a lovable, easy-to-care-for angel. Get plenty of rest, because once she starts to crawl, you'll soon need all the energy you can muster.

YOU'VE COME A LONG WAY
Phase V - 8 to 14 months

There is a particularly important transition period, which for most children occurs between seven and eight months of age, when in my judgment children move from a time of life when very good development is highly likely to a time when very good development is easily interfered with. If I'm right, you, as your baby's teacher, ought to be aware of this change, especially since you can cope successfully with the situation if you are prepared for it.

A baby about to enter Phase V (8 to 14 months) is far more talented than a newborn. If you think back for a moment to those early days in the life of your child and compare him then with what he is now, you can't help but be impressed. Think first of the change in sociability. Now it's certainly OK to admit that a newborn baby is not all that sociable. When you think back to those first sleepless weeks and compare them to those from the third month on, the growth in social interest and above all in responsiveness has surely been impressive.

Remember, also, how limited were your new baby's skills in looking and hearing; how alert she gradually became after those first two months; how alert she is now to the sights and sounds around her. Note, especially, how far she has come in her ability to control her body. Can you recall how floppy her head was, and how her arms waved so abruptly, indeed almost wildly? Now she has firm head control and can reach with accuracy for anything nearby. Now she can turn over easily and sit comfortably.

Let me point out, however, how much further your baby has to go in some areas. While vision and hearing skills have reached mature levels, clearly your baby is still quite limited in mastery of her body. Crawling may or may not have begun; pulling to stand, climbing, and walking, usually have not.

It is interesting to realize that those human activities which most clearly distinguish us from other animals are the least well-developed at this time. It is a rare Phase IV child (5 to 8 months) who speaks, although one or two words may very well be understood. There is no reason to believe that a baby at this stage has any thinking ability or intelligence of consequence. The most complicated problems such children can solve involve pushing an obstacle aside in order to get to a desired object. As far as we know, Phase IV babies (5 to 8 months) have very little memory or understanding of the world around them. Beyond crying to get your attention, there's little evidence of social skill in such young babies. While each baby is unique, the personality of a Phase IV child is very simple compared to that of a two- or three-year-old.

In summary then, the baby about to enter Phase V (8 to 14 months) has come a long way but still has quite a way to go. The abilities he has acquired are both very basic and, as far as learning is concerned, very likely to be acquired except under unusual child-rearing conditions. In other words, most parents, rich or poor, well-informed or not, end up with "well-educated" Phase IV babies. If you follow the instructions given here, your children will probably be somewhat advanced, but even if you knew very little about raising babies, yours would still acquire most of what could be acquired during those first months. You can interfere with the development of vision if you try hard enough. You can also teach a child not to cry for attention by simply ignoring her during her first months, but of course, most people don't treat their babies that way. In fact, parents acting naturally usually provide their babies with a very good basic education during the first eight months of life. But the story often changes as the baby approaches the eighth month if parents continue to rely solely on common sense as their primary guide.

Why should that be?

By the time babies reach eight months of age, most of them have acquired the ability to move around on their own. The usual way is by crawling, although some may scoot or even drag themselves forward, using their arms more than their legs. A baby who has just learned to crawl quickly becomes much more trouble than he had

been. Crawling babies can easily get hurt. Most homes are full of hazards for such children. Electric cords—when pulled or leaned on—are bad news. If the insulation is broken, burns or shock can result. Anything small (less than 1½ inches in one dimension) can cause trouble. Think of how many such small items every home contains. Crawling babies spend a lot of time on the floor, and they try to put most things they come across into their mouths. If an adult discovers a piece of broken glass on the floor, he carefully disposes of it. If a ten-month-old finds one, the response is different—and extremely dangerous.

Crawling babies are clumsy and inexperienced. They don't know what's safe to lean on. They don't know how doors work. The list of dangers is very long. But that's not all. Crawling babies are also messy and destructive. They don't clean up anything. In fact, they seem to enjoy wallowing in litter. The fact that you've nursed a plant for months won't stop a baby from destroying it in minutes.

The danger, extra work, damage, and aggravation together mean stress and work. What should parents do? Many respond to this situation by using playpens or other restrictive devices to keep the newly crawling baby in one small space. While such methods do reduce the danger, stress, and work, they also seem to interfere with the child's development. What can you do?

Babies are designed to want to learn and develop. Nothing that lives, including a kitten, is more curious about the world and eager to learn than a newly crawling baby. That curiosity first shown in the Phase II (6 weeks to 3½ months) baby's interest in faces and her own hands is the key element in early learning. Preserving and expanding it is very important. Fortunately, it's easy and fun to nurture a baby's curiosity. If you've followed my advice and have made your home as hazard-free as possible, and if you've moved your valuable breakables out of reach, you can now

give your Phase V (8 to 14 months) crawler a wonderful gift by simply turning her loose. You won't have to urge her to explore. That's what Phase V babies are naturally inclined to do. But, oh, how useful you can be.

Preserving and Expanding Curiosity

By offering your home to your baby, you have instantly provided a vast number of interesting things to do. The crawler will, first of all, very much enjoy just getting around. Remember, for many weeks she's been looking and listening but unable to get to the many attractive places and things *all* homes have. A kitchen cabinet is a wonderland for a nine-month-old. Playing with canned goods, plastic containers, pots, and pans is great fun, and anything that's great fun for a baby is usually educationally appropriate. Just practicing crawling is very enjoyable for a baby. As she gets a bit older and can stand and climb, the opportunity to look out the window provides yet another dimension.

Water is endlessly fascinating at this stage. Providing an inch or two (more might be dangerous) in a wading pool or other suitable container, along with plastic cups or pitchers for pouring water back and forth, entertains the baby. Simple mechanisms are very appealing too. The action of a light switch or better yet, an instant-on radio or television set, is fascinating. Lucky is the baby who is given the chance to flush the toilet (provided it's easy to work).

Phase V babies (8 to 14 months) are also fascinated by hinged objects. They love to swing the hinges back and forth. Hinged objects can be as large as full-sized doors or as small as a two-inch lid on a small toy. Babies enjoy the motion and the skill involved in producing that motion. Balls of various sizes and shapes are also fascinating now; they not only move in interesting fashion but also move a great deal for a very little effort.

Phase V babies love playing with collections of objects in containers and covering containers with lids, provided the covering task is not too difficult for them. They like to fit objects into each other as well as on to one another.

Most of these materials and mechanisms are in everyone's home, so no expense is involved in providing such valuable experiences for babies. There are also commercial toys that can be useful, especially for those inevitable times when a baby seems bored or is necessarily confined for any length of time. If, for example, you're taking the child on an auto trip or if you're visiting a home that hasn't been baby-proofed, traveling with a few attractive toys is a good idea. For the Phase V baby (8 to 14 months) the following toys are genuinely appealing:

Crib activity toy or box
Bath toys for water play
Books with stiff pages
Toy telephones
Large, inflatable plastic beach balls.

Small objects, windows, hinged objects, mechanisms, good toys, places to go in and out of the home—all play a part in feeding the baby's curiosity. (In case you're wondering, television does not, as yet.) Another major ingredient that's needed, however, is you. Babies develop best when there is someone who is totally involved with them and who is nearby *for many hours each day* to share their excitement, help when help is needed, and especially to talk

about what's happening.

As a teacher, then, your job has two major dimensions: your indirect influence on the baby, and your direct influence. When you safety-proof your home and then let your Phase V (8 to 14 months) baby explore it, the experiences that follow will have been made possible by you. But even if you are not actively involved as the baby explores the contents of the pantry, you have made that experience possible by scheduling the day's activities. Your direct influence comes when you are actually interacting with the baby. I recommend the following interaction style.

1) Expect to be approached by your Phase V (8 to 14 months) baby more than you approach him (at least seven or eight times each hour).

2) When he approaches, respond quickly.

3) If he approaches at an awkward time, respond quickly but tell him he'll have to wait to get your full attention.

4) Look to see what's on his mind.

5) Talk in ordinary, full sentences (with a simple vocabulary).

6) Be spontaneous abut related ideas, e.g., "Yes, Daddy has a big car just like yours!"

7) Don't hold on when he wants to leave for something else to do.

Such behavior on your part will lead to deeper curiosity, more pleasure in exploration, and good language learning.

Teaching Language

Curiosity is the major force behind learning. Language is one critical ability that should be learned well during the first years of life. *How well it is learned depends directly on you.* I don't mean to alarm you, but it is a fact that parents are the key to early language learning. Furthermore, by the time she's three years old, your child should be able to understand and communicate effectively. To give you some idea of how well, she should understand about 1,000 of the most common words by her third birthday. Right now, between the ages of about eight to twelve months, these are the first words she's likely to understand:

Mommy
Daddy
names of family members and pets—often known idio-
    syncratically ("doody" for Judy)
bye-bye
baby
shoe
ball
cookie (sometimes idiosyncratically)
juice
no-no
wave bye-bye

Besides the fundamental role that language plays in the development of intelligence, it plays an extremely important part in the development of social skills. So much of what transpires between any two people involves either listening to or expressing language. So in a very significant way, good language development underlies good social development.

Even if you make no special effort, your child will probably learn a good deal of language during her first years. If, however, you know what you are doing as her first teacher of language, I promise you she will *learn more*.

First of all, make sure she continues to be able to hear well. If she regularly becomes congested due to allergies or colds or infections, language learning is likely to be negatively affected. Keep her as healthy as possible in this regard, and follow up any concern with a visit to a pediatric audiologist if possible.

Next, follow my advice on nurturing curiosity. This is important because it is the interested, involved child who is the best student of language.

Then use the response style I've described. Be careful to use language in relation to the here and now. Phase V babies (8 to 14 months) are concrete thinkers. They process information best when it relates to what they are involved in at the moment.

Begin to use picture books with the baby when he starts to show interest in the pictures as well as wanting to turn the pages. Until he's about fourteen months of age, expect him to be more interested in finger skill practice with books than in names for pictured things. Don't expect him to show interest in story themes at this time. That will happen in Phase VI (14 to 24 months).

Intelligence

During Phase V (8 to 14 months) intelligence grows. One sure sign is the growth of memory. Early in Phase V babies are easily distractible, and memory is very short-lived. By the end of Phase V, putting a baby in another room for five minutes will no longer wipe out the memory of a forbidden activity. What a pity! Nevertheless, most problem-solving during this phase is what the late Jean Piaget calls sensorymotor. It involves trial and error behavior rather than the comparison and judging of ideas.

According to Piaget (his classic work on early intelligence is *The Origins of Intelligence in Children*, W.W. Norton, Inc., New York, N.Y., 1963), the more objects and mechanisms a baby has access to at this time of life, the better he learns. Admittedly, however, neither Piaget nor I believe that the development of sensorymotor intelligence is at risk during the first years of life. The primary reason to provide for and encourage sensorymotor play is a motivational one. Children very much enjoy such play at this age, and it seems to heighten their natural "need to know."

Some people would suggest that you do much more about encouraging the growth of intelligence at this stage than I would. If you put enough effort into it, you might get a child to learn a bit faster than she might otherwise, but my preference is that you refrain from special programming at this age. Remember, there's more to a baby than budding intellect. This is also a special time in life for social development. Children acquire their first friends (their parents) and their first views of themselves during these early years. Too much attention to intellectual goals can interfere with social development. This is a unique time for parents to enjoy a baby and vice versa. Lengthy training sessions can interfere with that special pleasure and can spoil the time of the early parent-child relationships.

Teaching About People

During Phase V, VI, and VII (8 to 36 months), children receive their basic training about people. By the time they enter Phase V (8 to 14 months), they've already learned that the arrival of an older person usually means that discomfort will be reduced or pleasure will be increased. They've also learned that crying will often be followed by the arrival of an adult. Over the next 16 months (Phases V and VI) learning more about others and beginning to learn about themselves will be their highest priorities.

In addition to the ability to get attention, there are seven other important social skills during the first three years:

1) using an adult as a resource
2) expressing emotions to adults
3) showing pride in achievement
4) engaging in role play
5) competing with peers
6) expressing emotions to peers
7) leading and following peers.

The first four skills tend to appear during Phase V (8 to 14 months): the first two just before the first birthday, and the second pair just after the first birthday. It is easy to see how important parents are in respect to these skills. For example, crawling and climbing babies need help at times. They get themselves into places and situations that can frighten or frustrate them. At other times they'll simply want something they can't reach. Though they can't express their needs in well-developed speech, they can draw attention to themselves with noises and then use gestures to indicate what's on their mind. It's the most natural thing in the world for adults to want to help such a child even if she's not their own, but it's a more compelling situation if the child is your own or your grandchild. Routine assistance teaches an infant an important fact about

adults: they can help when a situation or need is beyond baby's capacity. However, this natural development of the last part of the first year of life is not guaranteed. It depends upon the ready availability of a concerned grownup for lengthy periods over many, many days. Sadly, some three-year-old children have learned *not* to ask for help.

Another social behavior that emerges toward the end of the first year of life is the expression of anger directed toward another person. In contrast to the undirected expressions of rage, which are common to all infants in distress, Phase V babies (8 to 14 months) make it clear at times that they are angry at you. They might not get to this behavior, but you should be prepared for it, and I believe you should consider it as a sign of good development, provided such moments are less common than expressions of affection.

Shortly after the first birthday, as a result of mental development, children begin to engage in "make believe" or pretend episodes. One such common situation involves pretend telephone conversations. Other examples feature an imitation of mother's activities such as housekeeping chores or baking. The sight of an infant, barely able to talk but mimicking adult behavior, is great fun. I urge you to enjoy and encourage such behavior. If a loving adult spends a lot of time with a Phase V baby (8 to 14 months), reinforcement of such behavior is almost inevitable.

At about the same time, infants begin to show pride in their achievements. Starting at about eight months and continuing until two years of age, they become extremely interested in the responses of other people to their own behavior. Especially for first-time parents, the dramatic motor achievements of the period between seven and eleven months of age are very exciting. First, the baby learns to pull herself to a sitting position without help. Then, in the weeks that follow, she becomes able to crawl, to pull to stand, to climb upstairs, to walk while holding on, to climb down stairs and off of sofas, and then to walk unaided. This mastery of the body to the point where the child can move around comfortably on her own has enormous importance to the baby and is a source of pleasure to both the infant and parents. The joy in genuine achievement—combined with the child's rapidly increasing concentration on the responses of the adults close to her—means that right from the beginning of the process, the appearance of each new skill, even though imperfect at first, produces a response from the adult and a glow of pleasure from the baby. Through a process of conditioning, by the time the child is twelve or thirteen months of age, she has come to anticipate attention, excitement, and compliments when she does something new or difficult. After having done something relatively marvelous, she will turn immediately toward the adults she knows, in anticipation of praise. Here, then, is the time in life when pride in genuine achievements first appears and can be encouraged. Once again the magic ingredient is the presence of at least one adult with a very special feeling for the child.

It is easy to see how much there is to teach a Phase V baby (8 to 14 months) about people. It is also clear that this kind of teaching is both easy and very enjoyable. Indeed I doubt that you'll get more pleasure out of many other kinds of experiences in life.

A PERSON IS EMERGING
Phase VI-14 to 24 months

Phase VI is for parents perhaps the single most difficult period of a child's early years. The most striking qualities of this stage are the growth of individuality or personality and the struggles with authority that normally occur. Along with rapid growth in intelligence and language, this is the time in life when children first become aware that they have power in their dealings with others. One sign of this new awareness is the use of the pronoun "mine." The clearest sign of this period, however, is the child's growing tendency to resist suggestions and directives—in other words, negativism. This preview of adolescence, though annoying, is a normal part of the early attachment process. Under most circumstances children work these issues through by their second birthday and then turn their attention to other matters such as social life with peers.

To ignore the power of the social developments of the fourteen- to twenty-four-month period would be a mistake. In the same way that understanding how a child's mind grows will make parenting richer and easier, understanding major social development will bring similar rewards.

During this time your child will probably start testing wills with you. But children who have been accustomed to occasional control and who are dealt with sensibly, firmly, and lovingly from eight to fifteen months, become used to the fact that they can't always have their own way. The result is that when normal negativism and testing of the wills surfaces, they are easier to live with than the overindulged child who has learned to ignore halfhearted prohibitions. The child treated with clear and reasonable limit-setting during the eight- to twenty-two-month-period will usually leave negativism early, having had less difficulty resolving interpersonal conflicts, and return to smooth social relations by the second birthday. Even so, the six months that follow can be a difficult period for parents.

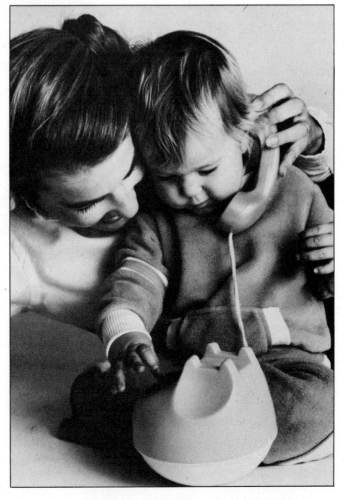

When studying children in their own homes, our researchers paid special attention to discipline and found that regardless of the family's income, cultural background, or educational level, firm discipline always accompanied good intellectual and social development. From the time the child began to crawl, his parents made sure that when a behavior was unsafe or unacceptable for other reasons, the infant received a clear and persistent message to that effect. In these homes telling the child not to do something was ordinarily not repeated more than once. Many parents, when noticing a behavior they disapprove of, say something to the baby but fail to make sure that he has really stopped the behavior. A momentary interruption can be counted on, but often as soon as the parent turns away, the baby returns to the forbidden act. It takes real effort to follow through on each such occasion. Yet all successful parents we have studied did so. Furthermore, as the weeks went by, such parents had an easier time of it than most because their babies gradually came to understand that their parents' words really had meaning. In contrast, with less effective parents, what the babies learned was that if they waited a few moments until the message was finished, they could go back to what they were doing.

If control has been firm though loving during the preceding months, the child will probably have figured out that his parents are in charge of the home, and he will be free to move on to other pastures. The social needs of Phase VI (14 to 24 months), which are visible in the "testing" and clinging behavior and in numerous other stressful ways, tend to interfere with the child's other interests. With those needs satisfied, the child enters into a more mature and easier style of relating to his parents. At the same time he begins to show genuine interest in children his own age.

Styles of discipline have to shift with the developmental level of the child because children change so rapidly throughout the first years. The second half of the second year of life is a particularly trying period for parents, and few get through it without several months of extra work. But firmness and consistency pay off now and in each successive stage.

Motivation

During Phase VI (14 to 24 months) you will begin to marvel at the amazing accomplishments of your child. You've already been impressed by the many achievements of the first fourteen months, but what surfaces during the balance of the second year of life is more dramatic for at least three reasons. First, the development of speech opens up communication in an almost miraculous way. Now, access to your baby's mind is actually possible. Second, that mind is becoming much more interesting and active than it has been. Signs of imagination and originality are blossoming. Your baby thinks things up! She asks questions and reveals a boundless curiosity at the same time she makes it clear she has been thinking. According to psychologist Piaget, active thinking becomes common between eighteen months and two years of age.

You can actually begin to see the mind working and the "wheels turning" in the behavior of the child toward the end of this phase. There are interesting delays in his behavior, and you can often predict his next act on the basis of the circumstances and his facial expression. His next behaviors often seem to confirm that he had actually been thinking out alternatives or at least had been dwelling on a particular move that he was going to make.

Third, the crystallization of a complicated personality proceeds at a very exciting pace now. The simple, lovable one-year-old becomes an impressively complicated two-year-old at a rate that parents can hardly prepare for and makes this a time of both wonder and importance.

The key to effective teaching at any age is motivation. If you can teach in a way that meshes well with your student's strongest interests, you'll have the greatest success. The Phase VI child (14 to 24 months) has the same major interests as the Phase V child (8 to 14 months). She is still very concerned with mastering her body, satisfying her curiosity, and, of course, coming to terms with the primary people in her life. Whereas in Phase V the first two interests were perhaps a bit stronger than the third, during this phase the social interest is strongest. And good development is reflected in the healthy maintenance of all three.

The new achievements of this particular period are especially rewarding to parents. This is the time when children begin holding real conversations with family members. Children are now moving from babyhood into the first forms of personhood. Their personalities are becoming clearer, more reliable, and more individualistic. And they are very much interested in you, the primary caretaker. All of this contributes to a general feeling that you are living with a young, very interesting person rather than with a baby.

If a Phase VI child (14 to 24 months) has access to most of the home and to an adult who's sensitive to how much learning is taking place, a high level of interest in learning is very likely. It can be enhanced by the availability of appropriate toys, by excursions out of the home, and by attention from other interested people. As Maria Montes-

sori, the famous educator and author, pointed out many years ago, it is the nature of the young child to want very much to learn.

Intellectual Development

Since interest in the person around whom the day revolves will affect most activities during this phase, it is comparatively easy (and very enjoyable) to help a Phase VI child (14 to 24 months) move forward intellectually. The first order of business is the completion of the development of sensorymotor intelligence—the simple problem-solving abilities that infants acquire before they become thinkers. This process is generally completed between eighteen and twenty-four months of age. It includes many understandings about the world of small, movable objects. The two-year-old realizes that objects have an existence of their own, whether he is playing with them or not. He knows much about how they move when they are thrown or dropped. He has learned a fair amount about causes and effects and about the sequences of activities. His memory, the capacity to retain mental images in the absence of the actual object, has grown remarkably.

Fortunately and interestingly, these remarkable mental abilities are acquired without any special parental efforts. It's hard for the parents to miss in this area. It is rather in two other areas of their child's mental development that parents have important contributions to make. The first is in the area of motivation—in nurturing the interest in learning. The second is in the development of higher mental abilities—the capacity to use ideas to think about the world and to solve problems.

According to Piaget's theories, the more things a Phase VI child (14 to 24 months) has seen and played with, the more he wants to see and play with. The process can be helped along even further if parents participate (at times) in these early explorations by providing an occasional new toy or situation when a baby seems bored; by sharing the excitement they experience in play and discovery; and by helping the child when he's stuck or needs other assistance. The parent's role is like that of a skillful Montessori teacher. She designs an interesting environment, allows the child access to it, then moves back, letting the child choose his activities for the most part, but being available to assist, encourage, and share the pleasures.

While most people tend to think of toddlers as primarily mother-oriented, the fact is that play with small objects occupies much more of their time. All social experiences combined will occupy from 10 to 20 percent of the day, while play with toys and small objects is likely to occupy at least twice as much time, especially early in Phase VI (14 to 24 months). This kind of play, encouraged by an adult, reinforces their interest in learning. At the same time they also learn much that will lead to more mature play during their third year. Exploring objects and practicing simple skills lead to more sophisticated play such as drawing pictures and creating scenes to support play with themes such as a visit to grandparents.

An actual visit or trip in the car, however, might be unsatisfying to children this age as they rarely look outside when riding in a car. Even when their car seat is positioned near a window, for some reason they show little or no interest in the passing scenery. Auto rides seem to be boring to young children, and since it is unsafe for a young child to be in a larger area, such as a portable playpen, in a moving car, toys can't be used to keep the child occupied. Picture or story books are not easily dealt with by a child in a car seat either, so you're left with conversation or talk of some sort to keep a child from being bored for the entire trip.

The best mental development also rests upon healthy intellectual curiosity about objects, their movements and qualities, and about how things work. In addition, it depends upon the ability of the mind to cope with abstractions (ideas) and also on language abilities (especially receptive abilities). During Phase VI (14 to 24 months) both capacities come into their own. At first, much of the language focused on the here and now is the primary route to good mental development. Gradually, toddlers reveal a new capacity: to deal with chains or sequences of ideas. As soon as such indications are present, simple stories become more interesting and useful to the child. Toward the end of Phase VI (14 to 24 months) simple conversations become possible, and, of course, they, too, can be helpful in encouraging mental growth. Encouraging role play or pretend behavior is especially recommended and is great fun for all concerned.

Expanding Language Skills

It is clear that you can't fully separate the topics of intellectual and linguistic development. In the sense that

you can't teach social skills to a baby without using language, neither can you assist mental development without it. It is relatively easy to help toddlers acquire excellent language skills. By excellent language skill, I don't necessarily mean excellent speech. A two-year-old is usually more accomplished in the area of receptive language than in speech. Typically, a two-year-old will have 200 to 275 words in his *spoken* vocabulary and understand over 300. Here are some of the most commonly understood words and phrases from twelve to fourteen months:

book	get up
bring (give mommy, me...)	hair
	hi
brush your hair	hug
car	kiss, kiss me
chair (highchair)	kitty (cat)
come here	patty cake
cracker	peekaboo
cup	sit up
dance	socks
dog (doggy)	stand up
drink	stop that
ears	throw the ball
eyes	water
feet	

The child from fourteen to eighteen months will probably add to his understanding these words and phrases:

apple	horse
bed	keep
blanket	let's go
bottle	milk
cereal	open, close the door
coat (jacket, sweater)	spoon
do you want...?	show me
don't touch	teeth
find	telephone (phone)
go get...	turn on (off) the light
hat	where is, are...

Though speech ordinarily blossoms during Phase VI (14 to 24 months), in some well-developing children it may be slow to develop until the third year (Phase VII). Furthermore, we have never figured out how to help a child begin to speak. The causes of delayed speech, when accompanied by poor development of understanding, are often identifiable, but such is not the case when the development of receptive language is normal.

The first order of business is your child's hearing ability. Regular checkups to be sure that there are no mild or moderate losses are very important. Parents are the most likely people (including pediatricians and nurses) to notice small hearing losses. If you suspect that your child is hard of hearing to any degree, be sure to follow up on the matter, and do not let anyone tell you that your baby will "grow out of" a suspected hearing loss.

If your child hears well, and if development has been good during the first year, language teaching is basically easy and lots of fun. Watch what the baby is interested in, and get into the habit of talking about that subject. When the toddler approaches you, it will usually be for help, for comforting, or to share an exciting discovery. At times it may be just to be near you. In most instances it's easy to tell what's on the baby's mind. Try to identify that interest, and then respond to it, using ordinary language.

You may be a naturally quiet person, or you may not be inclined to talk a lot to your baby until she talks more. Make a conscious effort to overcome the habit of silence. The more you talk to a baby about what he's interested in during the first years, the more skillful he'll become in language. It's really quite an easy process. Picture books will be useful during the early stages of Phase VI (14 to 24 months), and story books will come in handy toward the second birthday.

Threats to early language development include undetected small hearing losses, lack of regular sharing of experiences with caring adults, the failure of adults to talk much to preverbal babies, and the stifling of a baby's curiosity. All are easily avoided.

Don't count on television to do the job. Babies show little interest in television during the first two years of life. Even when they do pay attention to it, the television set can't compare with the individualized and enthusiastic input from a parent. He is better off hearing live language from you than listening to television.

If more than one language is spoken in the home and both languages are spoken well, the baby should be exposed to both from the beginning. Though she probably will be a bit slow in learning the languages, by the fourth or fifth birthday, she will be capable in both. No extensive research has yet been done on this topic, but authorities generally agree on this policy.

Play Group and Special Programs

Your Phase VI (14 to 24 months) child's progress will amaze you, and you may be tempted to seek ways of enhancing development even further through the use of educational programs. These may range from local pre-nursery-school sessions to special courses for parents. My general feeling about such efforts is that they may reduce everybody's pleasure in the growing process, but some parents feel strongly on this score. I have no doubt that with special effort, toddlers can be taught more than they usually would master and even some rather unusual skills. For example, advocates of the Suzuki method of teaching violin and piano recommend that training start during the first year of life! Whatever you decide, be aware of the cost to you in terms of time and money, and most of all, to your child. Don't persist in any special teaching efforts that result in a coerced, unhappy child.

To help a Phase VI child (14 to 24 months) continue to learn at her best, parents should keep an eye on their goals for the child and continue with the primary teaching tasks. I recommend that parents encourage balanced development in young children rather than overemphasizing intellectual precociousness. If intelligence, language, curiosity, and social skills are all growing well, the situation will be well in hand. As for the teaching tasks, providing new and interesting experiences, serving as the child's personal consultant, and guiding the child into good social relations by teaching reasonable and considerate behavior with others, are the major chores. Perhaps the most important lesson the child must learn is that she is very special but no more so than anyone else.

A THINKING BEING
Phase VII - 24 to 32 months

As with each of the preceding phases, Phase VII will find you dealing with yet another type of student. If all has gone well during the first two years, especially in the area of social development and monitoring of hearing ability, your child should be a remarkable person. First of all, she should have an impressive and complicated mind. Whereas younger children act out most of their experiences, Phase VII children think! They plot, plan, and reason. As you can imagine, there will be times when such skills make the child more difficult to handle. Of course, the thinking ability is still modest. As an example, consider this behavior. A two-year-old has spilled a glass of milk at the kitchen table while in full view of both parents. When her father asks her somewhat facetiously if she has spilled the milk, the child thinks for a moment and then somewhat guiltily says that her older sister did it. It doesn't take much to see that such a child is capable of constructing an alibi and yet still not very skillful at the task. This new capacity for reflection opens up many teaching opportunities.

Teaching becomes easier because the Phase VII child (24 to 36 months) is under much less social pressure, and teaching will also be affected by the crystallization of personality that has taken place. The individuality of the Phase VII child is much more pronounced and clear than it has been, and the child now becomes better at interpersonal relationships as she becomes more of an initiator within the family group. With rapidly increasing powers of expression and thought, her originality and capacity to learn combined with her strength of personality will all impress you mightily and make introducing her to new experiences even more exciting than before. Some parents enjoy this stage so much that they wish they could begin at the third year the second time around.

Insight, Intelligence, Imagination

At this stage of life, the child's memory is quite well developed. He is capable of insightful solutions to problems; that is, he can come up with answers—though not always the correct ones—by thinking rather than by trial and error. His capacity to think about the future and the past has begun to grow although he still does better when dealing with the here and now. Helping a child anticipate consequences by pointing out the next few events is a good idea during this period when his grasp of time and sequences is growing. Regular story sessions make sense now, and there are many first-rate books available for Phase VII children (24 to 36 months). Stories that capture the imagination and encourage fantasies are probably just as valuable as realistic ones. Our research on well-developed preschool children indicates that a rich fantasy life is one of their distinguishing characteristics; another is good observational ability. Staring steadily at something is a favorite activity of this age, so commenting on similarities and differences is a beneficial teaching habit.

Throughout this period I urge you not to smother your child with your teaching. That isn't necessary. If the child has interesting things to do, he'll be active. These suggestions about teaching are meant to describe an effective style but not to suggest that a parent should hover over a child or insist on many daily learning episodes. Most of the "teaching" we've observed has consisted of brief episodes that come up naturally as a part of the normal activities in a home. If you find yourself spending more than two hours of undivided attention with your Phase VII child, you're probably overdoing it.

In addition to stories, you can use toys, television, and outings as potentially valuable teaching aids. Toys that feature settings such as houses, farms, and stores along with furniture, people, and pets, are especially appropriate for this age child. In contrast, those that involve simple mechanisms, such as a jack-in-the-box, no longer offer much of a challenge. Puzzles of increasing difficulty are now very appealing, and there are many excellent ones available.

Many bright Phase VII children (24 to 36 months) become true fans of *Sesame Street*. In contrast to other television programs, this one has been skillfully designed to capture, hold briefly, and recapture the attention of three- and four-year-olds. (These methods work for many younger children as well.) *Sesame Street* will help your child learn numbers, colors, and other simple information. *I don't believe* that such experiences are "important" educationally, nor do I believe they convey any lasting impact. I recommend the program more for its value in broadening a child's interests. It is witty, entertaining, and informative, but in *no way* can it substitute for a loving human being sharing experiences with a child.

In the same way that viewing *Sesame Street* broadens the scope of a child's experiences, so, too, will trips out of the home. No longer is a trip to the supermarket a threat to your sanity. The Phase VII child (24 to 36 months), growing more and more civil every day, no longer "attacks" the contents of the market and can be a delightful companion, eager to hear your comments on the thousands of brightly colored items and the many interesting people.

I've emphasized providing interesting things to do as a part of an effective teaching style. The Phase VII child (24 to 36 months) has become quite familiar with the home if you've let her have access to it in the preceding year. So now the use of the home has to shift from a rich collection of exploratory sites to the place where lots of interesting things happen. The *events* of everyday life become more interesting than the physical environment. Looking out the window is still an interesting pastime, but more and more now Phase VII children want to learn about people, including other children, about activities like cooking and cleaning, and about making things themselves. They also welcome new physical challenges, like learning how to ride a tricycle or how to handle crayons and tools.

The majority of parents find it easy to keep a Phase VII child interested most of the day. Compared to dealing with a teenager, it's simple. That's because the Phase VII child (24 to 36 months) is not yet jaded about very much. Learning to operate a child's phonograph or any number of other gadgets still has a freshness about it. Seeing animals up close at a zoo, is, of course, being experienced for the *first* time. Watching an adult bake a cake can be fascinating experience for a thirty-month-old.

The Educational Significance of Nursery Schools

A discussion of interesting and challenging daily experiences leads to the question of more structured educational experiences such as nursery school. During a child's first two to two-and-one-half years, his parents are not only responsible for his development and well-being, but they are also his teachers. Sooner or later the teaching function will be shared with professionals. As the child approaches his second birthday, many parents start to think about nursery school. While a full treatment of the subject is not appropriate here, a few remarks seem desirable.

1) If a child is from a loving and caring family, she will suffer no educational loss if she doesn't attend a nursery school. As yet no nursery school has been shown to provide a lasting educational benefit to such a child.

2) A well-run nursery school can teach a child a wide variety of things, including how to read and write and even how to tie his shoelaces before the fifth birthday.

3) Children can encounter a wide variety of novel toys, equipment, activities, and people young and old at a nursery school. The result can be many challenging and pleasurable experiences.

4) If your two-and-one-half-year-old has a special educational need—for example, if he's language delayed—the typical nursery school is not the place for treatment. You'll have to seek out a special educational resource.

In the light of these remarks, what should you do? I recommend using nursery schools for the pleasure, variety, and stimulation they bring a child and for the "time off" they afford the parents. Parents should not assume, however, that there is anything vital to a child's educational career in the nursery school experience.

Teaching and Toys

Toys can be those items designed as toys or any objects children play with regardless of their intended use. Toys are a part of the lives of children from very early on and therefore an issue for parents.

During the first three years of a child's life, there are four rather distinct stages in respect to toys. In Stage 1, from birth to about seven months or so, children can't get around very much on their own. So during that stage toys can be very useful in helping to make the child's immediate surroundings interesting and instructive.

The next stage is from about seven to fourteen months of age. During that time children are normally excited and challenged by the process of mastering their bodies and especially in moving about and climbing. They find new vistas for exploration, and social development begins to proceed rapidly. Toys now play a smaller role in daily activities. There is simply too much to compete with.

Stage 3 occupies the rest of the second year, and it corresponds to Phase VI (14 to 24 months). Social development with the primary caretaker, usually his mother, tends to dominate the child's daily life. As a result, the toys of greatest interest to a child are those that are useful in social activities, especially those involving the person around whom the day revolves.

Stage 4 is the third year of life. With the growth of language, intelligence, imagination, memory, and interest in people, the role of toys is greatly expanded at this time.

As your baby's first teacher, what do you need in terms of equipment? Safety should be your paramount concern when choosing materials for use with infants and toddlers. Beware of poorly made materials. Beware especially of small objects that might become lodged in a baby's mouth. Objects that can become separated from larger objects are just as dangerous as individual small items. No object with a major dimension less than 1½ inches long is safe for an infant or toddler. Also be careful about paint used on toys and furniture for babies. Most paint being used today is safe. All lead-based paints must be avoided, and even though not much is used anymore, most older apartments and houses contain lead-based paints. Please note that though the top layer or layers of paint may not be lead-based, undercoats may be. Such paint, on window sills for example, has been a significant source of poisonings of children under three years of age.

The following chart should be a helpful guide to the selection of toys and other standard equipment for the first three years of life.

ITEM	AGE	PURPOSE	COMMENTS
A comfortable rocking chair	Birth to 3 years	To help you comfort a baby in distress For sheer enjoyment for both adult and baby	Close body contact while being moved rhythmically is enjoyed at all ages. It is particularly soothing to infants during the first months of life.
A safely constructed pacifier (about 6 of them)	Birth to 7 months	To help you comfort an uncomfortable baby	Specialists in pediatric dentistry see nothing wrong with use of a pacifier during the first year of life. Sucking, even when not followed by ingestion of fluids, is particularly soothing to infants.
A mobile that doesn't move (1 or more)	3 to 9 weeks only	To provide something attractive for the baby to look at when she's alone	Babies begin to show interest in the outside world toward the end of the first month so a mobile can be very appealing for a few weeks. Some mobiles are motorized and often include music boxes as well. Slow movement is especially interesting now, but no one knows whether the music has any effect.
A stainless steel mirror, minimum size 5 to 6″ in diameter, with no sharp edges	6 weeks to 6 months with occasional use for several additional months	To give the baby something interesting to look at	Both you and baby will have a great time with this item during baby's fourth month. Be sure to mount the mirror about 7″ from his eyes.
A crib gym or exercise toy	6 weeks to 6 months	To provide opportunities for the baby to have fun exploring his nearby world while learning to use his hands under the guidance of his eyes	Avoid those that suspend objects from strings—they tend to frustrate infants. Note: A child who sits up is too old for such items.

ITEM	AGE	PURPOSE	COMMENTS
An infant seat (make sure that it's well-made and stable)	3 to 6 months	To make it easy for you to move the small infant around the house	As head control gets better, babies enjoy looking at more and more of their surroundings. An infant seat increases the opportunity for adults and babies to play face-to-face games.
A crib activity toy or box	7 to 18 months	To help feed the baby's interest in operating simple gadgets To have something in reserve when the baby seems bored	A toy with lots of play value. It's almost indestructible.
Bath activity toy	7 to 24 months	Babies love water play. The variations are infinite.	This item has lots of play value, and it's very sturdy. However, don't forget to duck.
Books with stiff cardboard pages (about 6)	7 to 14 months	To feed the baby's interest in hand-eye practice and his fascination with hinged objects	Don't expect much interest in pictures or stories yet. As the child enters the middle of the second year, books can be used for more conventional purposes.
Balls (6–12) especially inflatable beach balls up to 24″ in diameter—the bigger the better. Soft sponge footballs	12 to 24 months and longer	*This is the single most popular toy during the second year of life.* Great for learning about the movements of objects. Great for practicing throwing, chasing, picking up, and carrying. Great for getting someone to play with you.	These are wonderful toys.
Pots and pans	6 to 12 months	To feed the child's curiosity about objects and sounds	No toy list would be complete without them.
Large, empty boxes	12 to 24 months	Just for fun	Great play value.
A playpen or play yard	5 to 15 months	To fill the need for a safe place to put a baby *for a few minutes;* for example, when the floor is drying or when a pot is boiling over. Don't, however, get into the habit of putting a child in a playpen for long periods of time.	The second syllable of this word is more accurate in describing the device than the first—play *pen.* Now there are narrower versions of the playpen, sometimes called play yards, that go through doorways and are quite portable.
Plastic containers with lids (empty ice cream containers are fine)	7 to 15 months	To feed the baby's strong interest in mastering hand-eye skills	These containers can also be used for water play. Babies in this age range are intrigued by their developing hand-eye skills. They enjoy removing and replacing lids on containers. Some frustration is likely.
A large plastic container with at least a dozen assorted, small but safe objects (i.e. thread spools, small plastic doodads)	7 to 15 months	To facilitate exploration of small objects and practice of hand-eye skills	Children seem enticed by "collections" of small items. They'll examine these, one at a time, or at other times they'll dump them all out at once.

ITEM	AGE	PURPOSE	COMMENTS
A stair gate	7 to 24 months	To allow stair climbing without anxiety or supervision, place the gate *on the third step*.	Supervise the baby's first attempts, and make a big fuss over her successes. Climbing *down* stairs is mastered several weeks after climbing *up* the stairs.
Scribbling and drawing materials (many)	24 to 36 months	To encourage drawing and use of writing implements	Representational drawing emerges during the third year, but don't be surprised if crayons sometimes get used on surfaces you'd rather not see used for this purpose.
Simple wooden puzzles (several)	24 to 36 months	To provide a simple challenge to intellectual and hand-eye skills	Keep the puzzles easy enough to sustain the child's interest. Some children get to be amazingly skillful at these—sometimes succeeding faster than adults.
Complete environment toys (school, airport, house) with miniature people and/or animals	12 to 36 months	To encourage imagination and fantasy activities—and for fun	Imagination and mental ability are now ready for play that involves organization and themes. For these and other reasons, this type of toy works.
A large, low container for water play outdoors	12 to 36 months	For feeling good on a hot day while at the same time encouraging hand-eye skills and curiosity	Lolling or splashing (under supervision) in a few inches of regularly replenished and refreshed water can be a taste of "heaven" for a child. Make sure that containers for pouring are also available.
A slide and climbing toy with ladder and play area under the platform	18 to 36 months	For fun and to help with the development of large muscle skills and mastery of the body	Interest in gymnastics stays high throughout these first years. This toy is well-made though expensive.
Small, hinged gadgets about 3″ high; doll-house furniture	7 to 15 months	To facilitate exploration of small objects and practice of hand-eye skills	Fine motor skills and hinged objects go together.
A toy telephone	12 to 36 months	To mesh with the emerging interest in make-believe activity	The baby will have great fun with this toy.
Small, *low*, 4-wheeled toys to be sat upon or straddled	14 to 30 months	To facilitate mastery of large muscle skills	They work.
Dolls and doll carriages	14 to 36 months	To feed a rapidly growing imagination	Validated by time.
An outdoor swing	12 to 36 months	For simple pleasure	Being swung through the air is an activity that most children love. Make sure the swing is sturdy.
Story and picture books (the more the better—about 20)	18 to 36 months	To support the development of language, curiosity, and a healthy social life	Language achievement levels are now suited to story-telling. The child's strong social interest during the second year heightens this pleasure. The child will show very little sustained interest until 18 months of age.

SUMMARY

If all has gone well, your three-year-old will be a marvelous human being with many or all of the following characteristics:

She should have an impressive mind, especially in respect to abstract thinking abilities. What do I mean by abstract thinking abilities? Basically, I'm referring to the capacity to deal with ideas, to be able to compare and contrast them, to string them together into related sequences. In short, to be capable of using "mental manipulations" to solve problems or simply reflect on or think about people, objects and events in the absence of concrete representations of them. One of the common signs of such skills is the capacity to be a good observer. Such observations may be of physical scenes, like a new hairstyle, or of the logic (or lack of it) in stories told by another person.

Another sign of good mental development in a three-year-old is the ability to predict upcoming events—for example, where a younger brother is heading and what may result from his trip. Yet another sign is a dawning ability to view the world from the point of view of another person. The child should show signs of a rich and vivid imagination. Involvement with ongoing conversations should be frequent, spontaneous, and interesting. She should be able to organize activities that are required in order to get a simple job done, such as procuring something to sit on, something to draw on, and something to draw with when she wants to color. She should be able to make use of substitutes when a conventional tool isn't available. For example, she should be able to use a fork instead of a spoon to stir a mixture or a hubcap to hold water if a bowl isn't handy.

The social style of a nicely developed three-year-old is delightful and interesting. Whereas some three-year-olds are afraid of adults they do not know, well-developed children tend to be comfortable with most people. They expect adults to like them, to want to help, and in general to treat them as almost equals. Conversation comes easily to such children. And they are not the least bit self-conscious about engaging in talk with total strangers. One accompaniment of such attitudes is a willingness to ask for help from any older person. However, assistance is only requested after it is clear to the child that the task at hand is too difficult for him to handle alone. Self-reliance and pride are two characteristics of such children. They also tend to be confident of their ability to do a "good job." With peers they move comfortably whether their role at the moment is to lead or to go along with the suggestions of another. Finally, if your child is one of the sort I'm describing, she'll be a warm and loving child, fully capable of expressing a full range of emotions, including minor displeasure as well as excitement and affection.

Should you be a parent of one of these children—and this is not beyond the abilities of most adults—you will be blessed in a most special way. Life has few rewards more valuable or substantial than those that come from living with a beautifully developed three-year-old. □

reaching & grasping

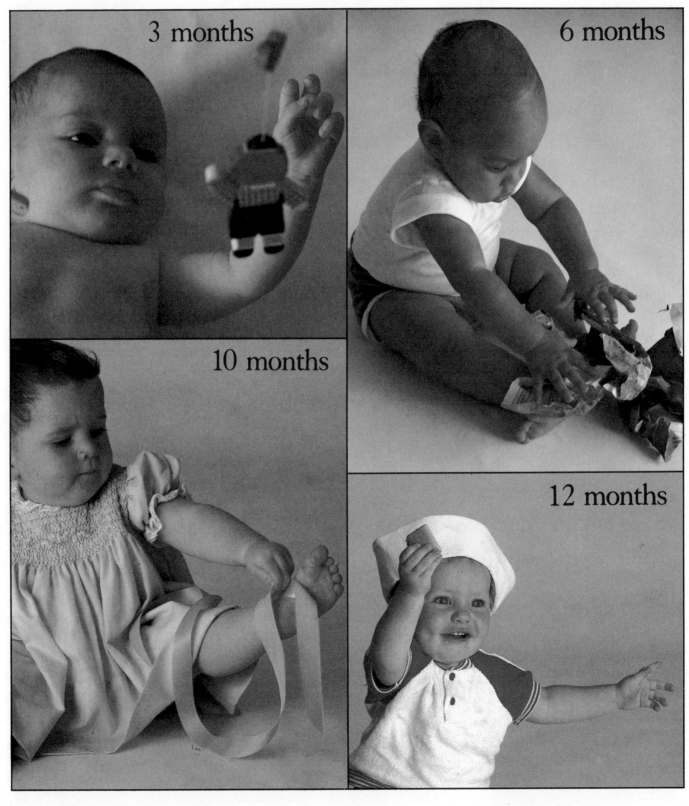

3 months

6 months

10 months

12 months

growth chart

Here and on the next few pages you will find special fill-in charts for recording your baby's growth and development through the first twelve months.

	WEIGHT lbs.	ozs.	**HEIGHT** ft.	in.	**CIRCUMFERENCE** head	chest
at birth						
1 month						
2 months						
3 months						
4 months						
5 months						
6 months						
7 months						
8 months						
9 months						
10 months						
11 months						
12 months						

milestones in baby's development

The first smile, tooth and step are big events in your baby's development. Record his progress here by filling in the descriptions and dates of some of these important "firsts."

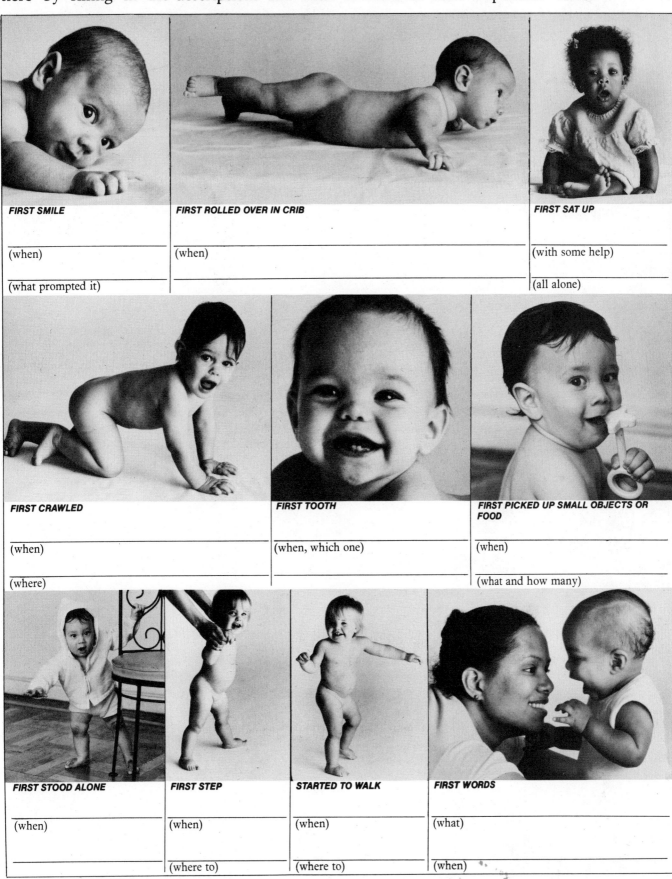

FIRST SMILE

(when)

(what prompted it)

FIRST ROLLED OVER IN CRIB

(when)

FIRST SAT UP

(with some help)

(all alone)

FIRST CRAWLED

(when)

(where)

FIRST TOOTH

(when, which one)

FIRST PICKED UP SMALL OBJECTS OR FOOD

(when)

(what and how many)

FIRST STOOD ALONE

(when)

FIRST STEP

(when)

(where to)

STARTED TO WALK

(when)

(where to)

FIRST WORDS

(what)

(when)

immunization record

It is vital that you take your baby to the pediatrician for immunizations against these preventable diseases. The American Academy of Pediatrics recommends the following schedule for the first 18 months. Keep a record here of each of your baby's immunizations and the date received. (For immunizations needed later check with your pediatrician.)

DATE OF BABY'S BIRTH_____

AGE	IMMUNIZATION	DATE RECEIVED
2 months	DTP diphtheria, tetanus, pertussis (whooping cough)	
	Polio	
4 months	DTP	
	Polio	
6 months	DTP	
1 year	TB test	
15 months	Measles	
	Rubella (German measles)	
	Mumps	
1½ years	DTP	
	Polio	